£58

Sabine Christiane Girod
Tumor Suppressor Genes and Cell Proliferation
in the Carcinogenesis of the Oral Mucosa

Editor-in-Chief:
Prof. Dr. Dr. Eberhard Krüger, Bonn, Germany

Tumor Suppressor Genes and Cell Proliferation Control in the Carcinogenesis of the Oral Mucosa

Dr. med. Dr. med. dent. Sabine Christiane Girod, Bonn

Quintessenz Verlags GmbH

Berlin, Chicago, London, Paris, Barcelona, São Paulo, Tokyo, Moscow, Prague, and Warsaw

From the Department of Maxillofacial Surgery
(Head: Prof. Dr. Dr. H.-D. Pape)
at the Medical Center of the University of Cologne, Germany.

Inaugural dissertation to obtain the "venia legendi,"
submitted to the Medical Faculty of the University of Cologne, Germany.

Author's address:
Klinik und Poliklinik für Mund-, Kiefer-, Gesichtschirurgie
der Universität zu Köln
Joseph-Stelzmann-Straße 9
D–50931 Köln

Die Deutsche Bibliothek – CIP-Einheitsaufnahme

Girod, Sabine Christiane:
Tumor suppressor genes and cell proliferation control in the carcinogenesis
of the oral mucosa / Sabine Christiane Girod. – Berlin ; Chicago ;
London ; Paris ; Barcelona ; São Paulo ; Tokyo ; Moscow ; Prague ;
Warsaw ; Quintessenz-Verl., 1999
   (Habilitationsschriften der Zahn-, Mund- und Kieferheilkunde)
   Zugl.: Köln, Univ., Habil.-Schr.
   ISBN 3-87652-936-0

Printing and Binding: Karl Wolf Offsetdruck, Heidenheim
Printed in Germany

ISBN 3-87652-936-0

Acknowledgment

I would like to thank Professor Dr. Dr. Pape, Director of the Department of Oral and Maxillofacial Surgery of the University of Cologne, for the continuous support of my work during the last years. Without the help of Professor Dr. Fischer, Director of the Institute of Pathology of the University of Cologne, and Professor Dr. Krüger, who generously accommodated me and my group in their laboratories, my research work would not have been possible.

The cooperation and scientific discussions with Professor Dr. Krüger and Dr. Petra Pfeiffer, University of Cologne, Professor Dr. Rollins and Professor Dr. Kaelin, Dana-Farber Cancer Institute, Boston, and Dr. Magnus Pfahl, San Diego Cancer Research Foundation, have been very enlightening and fruitful, and I would like to especially thank them all.

It has been a great pleasure to work with Ute Fischer, Ilona Leitner and Monika Junk, the technician in our group, and I would like to thank them and all the doctoral students for their dedication, enthusiasm and very hard work.

Ms. C. Müller, photographer of the Department of Oral and Maxillofacial Surgery, developed the pictures that are published herein.

My research has been supported by grants of the Deutsche Forschungsgemeinschaft, the Mildred-Scheel-Stiftung, the Moritz-Stiftung and the University of Cologne. A Lise-Meitner Habilitationsstipendium of the government of Northrhine-Westphalia enabled me to carry out my scientific work in the last three years.

Contents

1.   Introduction

"For the moment, we have little evidence that any oncogene or tumor suppressor gene has an elusive assignment in tumorigenesis. (...) Nevertheless, the search for genetic damage in cancer cells and the explication of how the damage affects biochemical function have become our best hope to understand, and thus to thwart, the ravages of cancer."

J. M. Bishop in Cell 64, 235-248 (1991)

Epithelial cancers of the aerodigestive tract account for one third of all cancer deaths each year. The development of squamous cell carcinomas in this region is closely connected with tobacco smoking and alcohol consumption. These exogenous factors are believed to play a major role in the complex multistep process of carcinogenesis in the aerodigestive tract epithelium. The induction of biologic and clinical changes in the epithelium of the oropharnyx, larynx, esophagus, trachea, and the lungs by common carcinogens has been termed field cancerization. The incidence of second primary tumors is especially high in head and neck cancers, presumably because of the diffuse mucosal initiation and promotion by exogenous factors such as alcohol and tobacco. Although oral squamous cell carcinomas account for only a small portion of cancers, they provide an excellent model system for the study of genetic changes. All histopathologic stages and their morphologic appearance during carcinogenesis in the oral epithelium are well defined and can easily be monitored without the need for invasive procedures. The current knowledge about epidemiology, etiology, and histopathology of benign and malignant oral lesions will be summarized in chapter 2 of this volume.

While recent advances in therapeutic management have improved the prognosis in some human tumors, others, such as squamous cell carcinomas arising in the upper aerodigestive tract, seem to be less sensitive to current therapeutic regimens. Patients with tumors of the oropharynx must not only face a life-threatening disease, they also have to cope with the prospect of a potentially disfiguring treatment despite great advances in reconstructive surgery. The standard multimodal treatment of oral squamous cell carcinomas today involves surgery in combination with radiation therapy and/or chemotherapy. Despite encouraging response rates in new combination therapies, the mortality rate for head and neck squamous cell carcinomas has remained almost unchanged during the last 30 years.

Oral carcinogenesis appears to be a multistep process similar to that shown in other human tumors. Tumor formation is almost certainly a consequence of accumulated genetic changes in oral epithelial cells. The possibility of a genetic predisposition in some cases is suggested by the sporadic occurrence of head and neck squamous cell carcinomas in young, nonsmoking adults, though genetics is an unlikely explanation in the majority of cases. In recent years two groups of genes, oncogenes and tumor suppressor genes, have been discovered. These genes play an important role in the control of cell proliferation and the development of the malignant phenotype. Oncogenes are the cellular counterparts of viral oncogenes that in general promote cell growth, whereas tumor suppressor genes act as dominant suppressors of malignancies.

Loss of function of the p53 tumor suppressor gene is involved in nearly all human cancers. The vital role of the p53 gene has been defined as a "guardian of the genome." By interacting with proteins of the cell cycle machinery, p53 mediates cell-cycle arrest, allowing for repair of damaged DNA, or cell death. The retinoblastoma tumor suppressor gene (Rb) encodes a nuclear phosphoprotein that is found in a mutated form in a wide range of human tumors.

Rb plays an important role in the control of cell division and differentiation and seems to be ubiquitously expressed in normal human tissue, including oral squamous epithelium.

Recent developments in molecular biology techniques have made it possible to study basic cellular mechanisms during malignant transformation and growth. For further progress in the diagnosis and treatment of oral preneoplastic and neoplastic lesions, it is important that the action of cancer-related genes in cell growth control and differentiation be understood. The current knowledge and the most recent results concerning the role of tumor suppressor genes in oral carcinogenesis are described in chapters 2, 3, and 4. Chapter 5 discusses the importance of understanding the basic principles of oral carcinogenesis and the application of molecular biology techniques in the diagnosis of the disease and patient follow-up for the development of new and more successful therapeutic strategies in oral premalignancies and oral cancer.

2. Literature Review

2.1. Epidemiology, Etiology, and Histopathology of Benign and Malignant Oral Lesions

The epithelium of the oropharynx is constantly exposed to a variety of exogenous influences due to the intake of food and the exchange of air. The epithelium of the lips, the cheeks, the floor of the mouth, the ventral part of the tongue, and the soft palate as well as the tracheo-bronchial tract is nonkeratinizing (Eversole 1989; Jetten 1989; Ohayoun et al 1985; Schroeder 1981). Smaller areas of the oral cavity where the mucosa overlies bone, such as the gingiva, the hard palate, and the dorsum of the tongue, consist of keratinizing cornified epithelium. A balance exists between cellular proliferation and differentiation. Usually keratinizing squamous cell differentiation in the upper aerodigestive tract is an abnormal differentiation in response to vitamin A deficiency as well as to toxic or mechanical injury (Lotan 1993). Hyperkeratotic lesions such as oral leukoplakia or in some cases oral lichen planus (OLP) can precede or be associated with oral squamous cell carcinoma (OSCC). Less than 10% of these lesions are highly dysplastic and at high risk of developing into cancer (McCarthy and Shklar 1980). Although this percentage seems small, it represents hundreds of thousands of patients worldwide. Further, OSCC is not always preceded by clinically obvious premalignant changes (Gundlach 1992; Koch 1974). Development of OSCC nevertheless seems to be a stepwise process connected with increasing dysplasia in the oral epithelium and accumulation of genetic changes.

The induction of generalized epithelial changes in the upper aerodigestive tract due to common carcinogens has been termed field cancerization (Slaughter et al 1953). The concept of multicentric origin of premalignant and malignant changes in this area explains the large percentage of patients who present with second primary tumors at different anatomic sites and the high incidence of locoregional recurrences in oral cancer.

It is well known that benign lesions in the oral mucosa such as lichen planus and leukoplakia differ greatly in their malignant potential. All stages of carcinogenesis in the oral cavity are readily accessible for observation during follow-up. The acquisition of gene defects in the control of differentiation and proliferation in the epithelium of the upper aerodigestive tract is believed to play an important role in the development of the malignant phenotype. The evaluation of genetic changes associated with the development of lichen planus, leukoplakia, and the malignant transformation into squamous cell carcinoma in the oral mucosa should therefore improve our understanding of the molecular mechanisms of oral carcinogenesis. Currently the search for genetic damage in cancer cells and the prevention of the disease by potent drugs, eg, retinoids, seem to be the most promising options to improve therapy and survival rate not only for OSCC, but for all carcinomas arising from the epithelium of the upper aerodigestive tract.

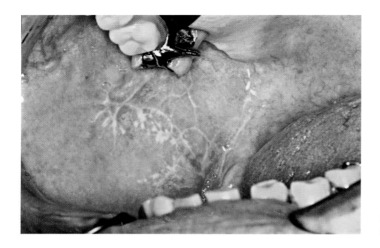

Figure 1:
Reticular Oral Lichen Planus

2.1.1. Benign Lesions in the Oral Mucosa

Oral Lichen Planus

Lichen planus is an inflammatory mucocutaneous disease which was first described by Erasmus Wilson in 1869. Wickham (1895) noted the striae atop the lesions that today still bear his name. The prevalence of oral lichen planus (OLP) varies between 0.02% and 2.6% among different populations (Bouqout 1986; reviewed in: Bouqout and Gorlin 1986; Eversole 1989; Laufer and Kuffer 1970; Murti et al 1986; Salem et al 1989; Schmidt 1961).

Oral lichen planus may be preceded, followed by, or accompanied by skin manifestations. Up to 53% of the patients with skin disease show oral lesions (Altman and Perry 1961; reviewed in: Boyd and Neldner 1991; Samman 1961; Schmidt 1961; Tompkins 1955; Wilson 1869). Between 4.2% and 44% of the patients with oral manifestations also demonstrate cutaneous lesions (Abramova 1968; Andreasen 1968; Axéll and Rundquist 1987; Cooke 1954; reviewed in: Eversole 1989; Kövesi and Bánóczy 1973; Konstantinov et al 1959; Lacy et al 1983; Renstrup and Pindborg 1958; Salem 1989; reviewed in: Scully and El-Kom 1985; Silvermann et al 1985; Sugár and Bánóczy 1959; reviewed in: Tyldesley 1974).

Oral lichen planus can appear clinically as reticulated (striae of Wickham), papular, plaquelike, atrophic, ulcerative/erosive, and combinations of those forms (reviewed in: Boyd and Neldner 1991; Bricker 1994; Eversole et al 1989; Scully and El-Kom 1985) (Fig. 1). The prevalence of the clinical forms of OLP varies greatly in different studies. The reticular and atrophic forms seem to be the most frequent. In most, but not all, studies erosive/ulcerative forms are less frequent (Abramova 1968; Altman and Perry 1961; Andreasen et al 1968; Axéll and Rundquist 1987; Bouqout and Gorlin 1986; Brown et al 1993; Cooke et al 1954; Hermann 1992; Kövesi and Bánóczy 1973; Neumann-Jensen et al 1977; Salem et al 1989; Silverman et al 1985; Thorn et al 1988; Tyldesley 1974). The widely varying and contradicting results of these studies concerning the prevalence of clinical forms of OLP may be explained by the facts that OLP seems to undergo changes in its clinical appearance during the course of the disease and that different clinical forms often occur simultaneously in the same patient (Abramova 1968; Barnard et al 1993; Pogrel and Weldon 1983; Thorn et al 1988).

According to most studies the buccal mucosa is the primary lesion site, with most lesions occurring bilaterally, followed by the gingiva and the tongue (Abramova 1968; Andreasen 1968; Axéll and Rundquist 1987; Bouqout and Gorlin 1986; Brown et al 1993; Gabriel et al 1985; Pindborg et al 1972; Salem et al 1989; Scully and El-Kom 1985; Silverman et al 1974; 1985; 1991; Tyldesley 1974). Reticular changes are usually asymptomatic, whereas erosive and ulcerative forms are associated with burning sensations and severe pain (Altman et al 1961; Andreasen 1968; Brown et al 1993; Eversole et al 1989; Silverman et al 1985, 1991).

Oral lichen planus is a chronic disease. Complete disease remissions with or without treatment can occur in up to 41% of the cases, with a better chance of spontaneous regression for reticular changes (Altman and Perry 1961; Andreasen 1968; Brown et al 1993; Eversole et al 1989; Kövesi and Bánóczy 1973; Neumann-Jensen et al 1977; Samman 1961; reviewed in: Scully and El-Kom 1985; Silverman et al 1985; Thorn et al 1988). In general the rate of spontaneous remissions is much smaller in OLP than in skin lesions. There is a predominance of female patients over male patients in OLP at a ratio of up to 2:1. Most cases occur in the fifth decade in men and the sixth decade in women (Axéll and Rundquist 1987; Andreasen 1968; Brown et al 1993; Herrmann 1992; Holmstrup et al 1988; Kövesi and Bánóczy 1973; reviewed in: Laufer and Kuffer 1970; Pindborg et al 1972; Salem et al 1989; Silverman and Griffith 1958; Silverman et al 1974, 1985, 1991; Thorn et al 1988; Tyldesley 1974; Vincent et al 1990).

The classic microscopic features of lichen planus include focal hyperorthokeratosis or hyperparakeratosis, acanthosis, and a dense bandlike lymphocytic infiltrate of the superficial stroma and the basement membrane. The epithelium does not show any indications for abnormal maturation and dysplasia. Liquefication of basal epithelial cells and the obfuscation of the epithelial-stromal interface is characteristic, leading to the saw-toothed configuration of the rete ridges (El-Laban and Kramer 1974; reviewed in: Scully and El-Kom 1985) (Fig. 9). The basal cell changes are accompanied by loss of desmosomes and hemidesmosomes such that the epithelium splits away from the basement membrane.

The precise nature of lichen planus is still unclear (reviewed in: Boyd and Neldner 1991; Scully and El-Kom 1985). An immunologic basis has been suggested because comparison with normal oral mucosa shows that the epithelium in the lesions has an increased number of Langerhans cells (Akasu et al 1993; Boisnic et al 1990; Cruchley et al 1989; Girod et al 1994d; Helm et al 1994; Lombardi et al 1993; Regezi et al 1985; Walsh et al 1990; van Loon et al 1989). Furthermore antigen expression of Langerhans cells appears to be elevated in OLP (Farthing et al 1990). The clinical manifestations of oral lichen planus seem to be related to the cell infiltrate and the integrity of the basal membrane (Hirota et al 1989). There is strong evidence that the primary mechanism of lesion development is that of T-cell-mediated immunologic interaction with basal epithelial cells perceived as foreign because of altered surface antigenicity (DePanfilis et al 1984; Eversole 1989; Hirota et al 1989; Junghell 1991; Shiohara 1988; Sugerman et al 1992; Walsh et al 1990). Recently E-cadherin, a cell-cell adhesion molecule, has been found to mediate interaction of epithelial cells with intraepithelial T-lymphocytes (Cepek et al 1994). The cell mediated immune response not only influences the epithelial structure in lichen planus, but also leads to a change in the extracellular matrix proteins in the upper connective tissue. These changes are likely to be connected with the loss of epithelial attachment and the development of erosions in lichen planus (Becker 1992; Sugerman et al 1993). Biochemical epithelial alteration coupled with genetic factors related to major histocompatibility profiles appear to render persons susceptible to LP or LP-like reactions (Regezi and Sciubba 1989; Porter et al 1993). Oral lichenoid reactions are also a feature of early chronic graft-versus-host disease, suggesting that there might be a common disease mechanism (Sugerman et al 1993).

The premalignant potential of OLP is still discussed controversially in the literature (Barnard et al 1993; Eisenberg and Krutchkoff 1992; Holmstrup 1992). Hallopeau (1910) first reported a case of malignant transformation of OLP in the maxilla. Since then a large number

Table 1: Malignant Transformation in Oral Lichen Planus

AUTHOR	YEAR	CASES	OSCC	MAL. TRANSF.
Williger	1924	20	10 % (2 cases)	–
Montgomery and Culver	1929	17	5.8 % (1 case)	19 months
Dechaume et al.	1957	50	10 % (5 cases)	40 yrs. (1)
Sugár and Bánóczy	1959	36	2.7 % (1 case)	13 yrs.
Warin	1960	53	9.4 % (5 cases)	up to 13 yrs.
Altman and Perry	1961	128	0.8 % (1 case)	12 yrs.
Rohde	1966	207	2.9 % (6 cases)	3.5 yrs. (1)
Jänner et al.	1967	150	4.6 % (7 cases)	up to 14 yrs.
Andreasen	1968	115	0	–
Abramova	1968	436	1.1 % (5 cases)	–
Shklar	1972	600	0.5 % (3 cases)	–
Kövesi and Bánóczy	1973	274	0.4 % (1 case)	–
Fulling	1973	225	1.3 % (3 cases)	up to 5 yrs.
Schirner et al.	1981	91	3.2 % (3 cases)	–
Silverman et al.	1985	570	1.2 % (7 cases)	2 yrs. to 7 yrs.
Murti et al.	1986	702	0.45 % (3 cases)	3 yrs. to 10 yrs.
Holmstrup et al.	1988	611	1.5 % (9 cases)	4.9 yrs. to 24 yrs.
Salem	1989	64	6 % (4 cases)	–
Sigurgeirsson and Lindelöf	1991	2071 (skin)	0.4 % (8 cases)	–
Silverman et al.	1991	214	2.3 % (8 cases)	1 yr. to 22 yrs.
Herrmann	1992	919	1.85 % (17 cases)	1 yr. to 12.5 yrs.
Voute	1992	113	2.6 % (3 cases)	5 yrs. to 9 yrs.
Brown et al.	1993	193	0	–
Barnard et al.	1993	241	3.7 % (9 cases)	–

of studies and case reports from different countries report a frequency of malignant changes from 0.4% to 10% after an observation period of up to 24 years (Table 1). In one case the patient reportedly suffered from OLP for 40 years before he developed an OSCC (Dechaume et al 1957). The differences regarding the frequency of malignant changes in OLP may be partly due to the fact that the diagnosis of lichen planus, especially in earlier studies, is based on clinical appearance only. Lichen planus may have been confused with dysplastic white lesions, eg, oral leukoplakia, which show a much higher rate of malignant transformation (Montgomery and Culver 1929; von Jänner et al 1967; Warin 1960). Although the issue of a routine biopsy in lichen planus cases is a controversial one, the possibility cannot be excluded that there are lesions that clinically resemble lichen planus and, by histopathology, show epithelial dysplasia, whereas others might not appear as lichen planus clinically but may show lichenoid changes by histopathology (Brown et al 1992; Reisman et al 1974). If lesions showing epithelial dysplasia were included in some studies, an incidence of malignant transformation close to that reported in oral leukoplakia can be explained.

In most studies in which a high incidence of malignant transformation is reported, the number of cases investigated is relatively small (Dechaume et al 1957; Salem 1989; Warin 1960; Williger 1924). In general, larger studies do not confirm the high incidence rates. According to those studies, malignant changes of OLP occur in 0.4% to 3.7% of the cases (Abramova 1968; Altman and Perry 1961; Barnard et al 1993; Cawson 1968; Fulling 1973; Holmstrup et al 1988; Kövesi and Bánóczy 1973; Montgomery and Culver 1929; Murti et al 1986; Rohde 1966; Schuermann et al 1939; Shklar 1972; Sigurgeirsson and Lindelöf 1991; Silverman et al 1985, 1991; von Jänner et al 1967; Voute et al 1992). In some studies no malignant conversion was found (Andreasen 1968; Brown et al 1993). It is possible that the follow-up period in those studies may have been too short for a relatively small number of cases. It has also been argued that the treatment modalities may cause a difference such that with a more aggressive treatment being employed by one of the groups, the small likelihood of malignant conversion decreases even more (Brown et al 1993). Nevertheless these studies support the view of some investigators who argue that there is insufficient evidence to prove that lichen planus is a premalignant lesion in the sense of leukoplakia and erythroplakia of the oral mucosa (Eisenberg and Krutchkoff 1992). According to these authors' earlier critical review of the literature, only 15 cases from 223 reported cases were accepted as malignant transformation of OLP (Krutchkoff et al 1978). Because exposure to known carcinogenic factors could not be ruled out from the medical history in any of those cases, the authors concluded that lichen planus does not have malignant potential. They acknowledged though that the disease may cause higher susceptibility to transformation by other carcinogens. Conversely there have been reports of malignant changes in OLP, in which the influence of known carcinogens could be ruled out (Girod et al 1993; Kaplan and Barnes 1985; Katz 1990; Lind et al 1985; Pogrel and Weldon 1983). In two of the cases oral squamous cell carcinoma developed during or shortly after treatment of erosive lichen planus with a retinoid (Girod et al 1993; Katz et al 1990).

Among the different locations, the tongue is at highest risk for malignant transformation (Barnard et al 1993; Holmstrup 1988; Katz et

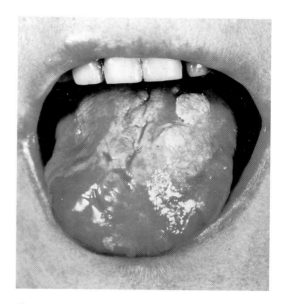

Figure 2: Erosive Lichen and Squamous Cell Carcinoma of the Tongue

al 1990; Kövesi and Bánóczy 1973; Silverman et al 1974, 1985, 1991) (Fig. 2). Out of 81 OSCCs from OLP that were documented in the literature and where the exact location had been described, 32 (40%) involved the tongue. Although OLP is predominantly found in the buccal mucosa, only 19 (23%) OSCCs were localized there. OLP of the gingiva and alveolar ridge is less frequent, and thus these locations seem to have a relatively higher risk of malignant development, with 16 (20%) OSSCs located there. Special attention has to be paid if LP occurs in the areas of the lips: although this is a rare location, 14 (17%) carcinomas were found there.

Atrophic and erosive lesions seem to be more likely to develop into OSCC (Faraci et al 1975; Jolly 1976; Kaplan and Barnes 1985; Lind et al 1985). Analysis of the available data reveals, though, that malignant transformation also occurs in a large number of patients who originally present with a reticular lesion. Some authors have described continuous changes in the clinical forms of OLP during the course of

15

the disease (Abramova 1968; Barnard et al 1993; Thorn et al 1988). It seems that some patients start out with reticular changes for example, and later develop erosive OLP, which then develops into OSCC (Barnard et al 1993). Erosive or atrophic lesions would thus present a more advanced or severe stage of the disease. Therefore, although OLP itself may not have any malignant potential, the pathologic changes in OLP may increase the vulnerability of the mucosa and predispose the epithelium to damage from carcinogenic agents regardless of the clinical presentation.

Although OLP is a disease that mostly affects women, the number of male smokers among those who develop a malignancy is increased up to fivefold in comparison with nonsmoking women (Barnard et al 1993; Gawkrodger et al 1994; Harland et al 1992; Krutchkoff et al 1978; Massa et al 1990; Sigurgeirsson and Lindelöf 1991). The predominance of smoking men among the cancer patients may also support the hypothesis that exogenous factors such as smoking and possibly alcohol consumption promote the development of carcinomas from OLP, where chronic inflammation is already present. It is well known that squamous cell carcinoma of the upper aerodigestive tract is a predominantly male disease associated with the higher rate of nicotine and alcohol consumption among men. Although OLP does not appear to be etiologically related to tobacco smoking, a higher prevalence of lichen planus was found among individuals with a tobacco chewing habit (Andreasen 1968; Axéll and Rundquist 1987; Kövesi and Bánóczy 1973; Murti et al 1986; Pindborg et al 1972; Salem et al 1989; Silverman et al 1958, 1985). A number of studies also indicate that chronic mechanical irritation from sharp teeth or ill fitting dentures may promote malignant changes, especially in reticular OLP (Montgomery and Culver 1929; Rohde 1969; Warin 1960). Kaplan and Barnes (1985) suggested that on a cellular level the increased turnover of basal cells in those lesions facilitates the development of a malignant clone in the presence of other promoters of malignancy.

It can be concluded from the currently available data that malignant conversion must be suspected in the management of OLP patients. The rate at which malignant changes occur is low and the latency is long, at least in comparison with other white oral lesions, eg, oral leukoplakia. As a result of the possible differences in clinical appearance and histopathologic diagnosis it seems advisable to confirm the diagnosis histopathologically when the patient is first seen. Although the rate of development of squamous cell carcinoma is low and it remains debatable whether or not lichen planus should be classified as a premalignant lesion of the oral mucosa, the patients should be followed up annually and possibly for life (Moncarz et al 1993). Special attention should be given to cases where atrophic or erosive lesions occur and when the tongue or the lips are involved, as these are the most likely forms and sites to develop carcinoma.

Oral Leukoplakia

Benign precursors of oral squamous cell carcinomas such as leukoplakia appear clinically as white patches or plaques that cannot be removed by scraping and cannot be characterized as any other disease (Axéll et al 1984; WHO 1978; Pindborg 1994). James Paget recognized the relation of oral white lesions with smoking more then a 100 years ago in 1870. The term leukoplakia was first used in Schwimmer's description of the condition in 1877.

As in oral squamous cell carcinoma, tobacco smoking and chewing can be regarded as the principal etiologic factors for oral leukoplakia (Andreasson et al 1984; Bouquot and Gorlin 1986; Creath et al 1991; Frerich et al 1992; Pindborg 1980; Reichardt et al 1987). Experimental studies and clinical data suggest that increased alcohol consumption may also play a role in the early pathogenesis of oral leukoplakia (Chiesa et al 1993; Eufinger et al 1992; Zöller 1992). Presumably because of differences in smoking habits, the prevalence of oral leukoplakia among men has usually been higher than among women, though the number of women seems to be increasing (Eufinger et al 1992; Waldron and Shafer 1975).

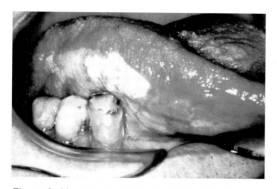 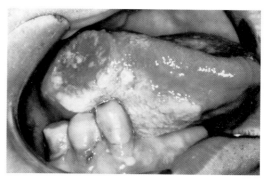

Figure 3: Homogenous Leukoplakia of the Tongue (Same patient as in Fig. 4)

Figure 4: Squamous Cell Carcinoma of the Tongue (Same patient as in Fig. 3)

A large number of studies from different countries also show marked geographic differences in the prevalence of oral leukoplakia, ranging from 0.4% to 29% (Atkinson et al 1964; Axéll 1976; Bánóczy and Csiba 1972; Bruszt 1962; Bouqout 1986; reviewed in: Bouqout and Gorlin 1986; Gangadharan and Paymaster 1971; Forlen et al 1965; Gerry et al 1952; Lay et al 1982; Metha et al 1969, 1981; Pindborg et al 1965a, 1965b, 1966; Reichardt et al 1987; Ross and Gross 1971; Silverman et al 1976; Wahi et al 1970; Waldron and Shafer 1975; Wilsch et al 1978; Zachariah et al 1966). The majority of lesions is found in the 40- to 70-year age group (Axéll 1976; reviewed in: Bouqout and Gorlin 1986; Dunsche et al 1992; Eufinger et al 1992; Schell and Schönberger 1987; Vesper et al 1992; Waldron and Shafer 1975).

The clinical classification of oral leukoplakia has been changed several times during the last decades and further adjustments are likely to occur as the knowledge about the disease increases (Axéll et al 1984; Sugár and Bánóczy 1959; Pindborg 1980a, 1980b; reviewed in: Pindborg 1994). Clinically, oral leukoplakia is divided into subtypes, with homogenous leukoplakia (Leukoplakia simplex) accounting for about 49% of all cases (Axéll 1976; Burkardt and Maerker 1981; Dunsche et al 1992). Homogenous leukoplakia is described as a usually asymptomatic white lesion with sharp margins and a smooth surface (Fig. 3). The development of malignant changes in these lesions is rare. Among the nonhomogenous forms of oral leukoplakia different subtypes are distinguished: erythroleukoplakia (erosive leukoplakia), nodular leukoplakia, and verrucous leukoplakia (Axéll et al 1984, Pindborg 1980a, 1980b). Erythroleukoplakia and nodular leukoplakia are also referred to as speckled leukoplakia and are often associated with Candida infection. Verrucous leukoplakia is described as an exophytic lesion with an irregular nodular surface. Erosive leukoplakia seems to have the highest potential of malignant development, though the correlations among clinical appearance, degree of dysplasia and malignant potential of the lesions are not very close. Therefore, most authors recommend biopsy be mandatory at the time of first diagnosis, regardless of the clinical appearance (Burkardt and Maerker 1981; McCarthy and Shklar 1980; Regezi and Sciubba 1989).

Because of field cancerization in the oral mucosa, leukoplakia can clinically appear to be confined to a particular anatomic site, eg, buccal mucosa or the floor of the mouth, or involve large areas of the mucosa (Slaughter et al 1953). The most frequently affected areas are the commissures and the buccal mucosa, followed by the gingiva, the tongue, the floor of the mouth and the palate (Eufinger et al 1992;

Bánóczy and Csiba 1972; Bouqout and Gorlin 1986; Dunsche et al 1992; Shklar 1986; Vesper et al 1992). The floor of the mouth and the ventral surface of the tongue seem to have the highest risk of malignant changes (Axéll 1976; Bánóczy and Csiba 1972; Bouqout and Gorlin 1986; Frerich et al 1992; Hogewind et al 1989; Regezi and Sciubba 1989). Benign leukoplakias seem to be preferentially located in the buccal region, while precancerous lesions and carcinoma dominate in the floor of the mouth and the tongue (Bouqout and Gorlin 1986; Hornstein et al 1981; Schell and Schönberger 1987; Tischendorf and Giehler 1990). This may be due either to the more volatile structure of the epithelium in these areas or longer exposure to carcinogens in the saliva (Schroeder 1981).

The histopathologic aspects of oral leukoplakia can vary from hyperplasia with hyperkeratosis without epithelial dysplasia, to various grades of epithelial dysplasia (Figs. 7, 11, 17, 18). In general the nonkeratinizing oral epithelium undergoes changes that resemble the differentiation pattern of keratinizing epithelium (Schroeder 1981). Features of epithelial dysplasia have been described by the WHO Collaborating Conference Center for Oral Precancerous Lesions (1978). The lesions are subdivided into mild, moderate, and severe dysplasia (Burkhardt et al 1978; Gräßel-Pietrusky and Hornstein 1982). In 1936 McCarthy recognized that the malignant potential of leukoplakia was correlated with clinical and microscopic features such as dysplasia of the epithelium, and consequently developed a grading system based on these features. Electron microscopy studies of preneoplastic lesions revealed subtle changes already present, similar to those in oral squamous cell carcinoma (Kannan et al 1993). The malignant transformation rate in oral leukoplakia differs greatly in various studies and has been reviewed extensively. The reported average rate ranges from 0.13% to18% (Bánóczy and Csiba 1972; Bschorer et al 1992; Cooke 1964; Dunsche et al 1992; Frerich et al 1992; reviewed in: Lind 1987; reviewed in: van der Waal 1992; Sugár and Bánóczy 1959; Tischendorf and Giehler

1990). Histopathologic evaluation of the lesions for presence or absence of dysplasia still seems to be the most reliable indicator for future carcinomatous development (Burkhardt and Maerker 1978; Burkhardt et al 1978; Lind 1987; Waldron and Shafer 1975). Leukoplakia with mild or moderate dysplasia only shows carcinomatous changes at a rate of 3% to 30%, whereas leukoplakias with severe dysplasia develop into OSCC in up to 43% of cases (Burkhardt und Maerker 1978; Frerich et al 1992). However, the correlation between clinical behavior and histologic appearance is not always very close. Using dysplasia grade as the only diagnostic parameter may be unreliable in predicting cancer development in individual cases because OSCC can also arise from nondysplastic leukoplakia (Dunsche et al 1992; Frerich et al 1992; Gundlach 1992).

The role of immunity and especially of antigen-presenting cells has also been discussed. The number of Langerhans cells increases during the carcinogenesis in the oral mucosa, and thus they may play a protective role in malignant transformation (Girod et al 1994d; Becker 1992).

In recent years viral infections, especially a high incidence of human papilloma virus (HPV), have been identified in OLP as well as in oral leukoplakia and squamous cell carcinoma (Cox et al 1993; Gassenmaier 1988; Jontell et al 1990; Milde-Langosch 1989; Miller et al 1994; Scully 1989, 1992; Thomas et al 1994; Yeudall 1992). It is well known that HPV infections play an important role in the development of genital tumors. The precise role of HPV in oral carcinogenesis, however, remains speculative. Human papillomavirus types 16 (HPV-16) and 18 (HPV-18) demonstrate oncogenicity by transforming normal human oral keratinocytes. While normal cells exhibit a limited lifespan, cells transformed by these viruses show immortality and altered morphology in comparison with their normal counterparts. The HPV-immortalized cells contain multiple copies of intact viral genome integrated into their chromosomes. However, the immortalized cell lines are nontumorigenic in nude mice (Park et al 1992). HPV infection may contribute to an increase in cell proliferation or immortalization of cells at an early stage of the disease. This could occur by compromising tumor suppressor genes involved in cell growth regulation such as Rb and p53. Thus HPV infection may be an additional factor responsible for the malignant transformation of benign or premalignant oral lesions.

2.1.2. Squamous Cell Carcinomas of the Oral Mucosa

Epithelial cancers of the oral cavity account for 1% to 4% of all cancers in the U.S. and Europe each year (Boring et al 1993; Gerson 1990) (Fig. 4). According to estimates of the National Cancer Institute of the United States, 29,800 new cases of oral cancer arose in 1993 resulting in 7,700 deaths. Wide variations exist in the incidence of oral cancer among geographic regions. Whereas carcinoma of the oral cavity constitute less than 4% of all cancer in America and Europe, in India up to 45% of cancers are oral squamous cell carcinoma (reviewed in: Kleinman et al 1993; reviewed in: Langdon 1985; Schottenfeld and Bergad 1985; Smith et al 1990). The incidence of mouth and tongue cancer has increased more than 50% from the 1940s to the 1980s (Gerson 1990; Smith et al 1990). In Germany the estimates of incidence and mortality of oral cancer are based on the death statistics. According to those statistics 7.8 cases of oral cancer occurred among 1,000,000 male inhabitants of the Saarland in 1990, whereas only 1.7 women suffered from the disease (Sellars 1979).

The development of squamous cell carcinomas in the upper aerodigestive tract is closely connected with prolonged exposure of the epithelium to known environmental factors, especially tobacco and alcohol. The incidence of second primary tumors presumably due to the diffuse mucosal initiation and promotion by exogenic factors such as alcohol and tobacco is especially high in head and neck cancers arising from the epithelium of the oropharynx and larynx, supporting the concept of field cancerization in the upper aerodigestive tract (Boysen and Loven 1993; Eckardt 1993; Enstrom 1988; Fijuth et al 1992; Hong et al 1985; Marchetta et al 1965; Parker and Schwartz et al 1994; Slaughter 1953; Vrabrec 1979; Tytor et al 1990).

Among practicing Mormons who neither smoke nor drink, cancer of the oral cavity and pharynx is nonexistent, whereas most patients with head and neck cancer have a history of heavy tobacco and alcohol abuse (Decker and Goldstein 1982; Marshall et al 1992). As long ago as 1795 Sommering realized the significance of pipe smoking in the development of lip cancer (Lickint 1930). The connection between increased tobacco consumption and development of squamous cell carcinoma of the upper aerodigestive tract was first described in the 1930s and has been confirmed in later studies (Graham et al 1977; Lickint 1930; Mashberg et al 1981; Rothman and Keller 1972; Schottenfeld 1979; Wynder and Bross 1957; reviewed in: Smith et al 1990). At the same time benzopyrene was identified as a carcinogen in tobacco smoke (Cook et al 1932). Later polycyclic hydrocarbons and N-nitrosamines were identified as the carcinogens in tobacco smoke (Dontenwill et al 1977; Wynder and Hoffmann 1968; Wynder and Mabuchi 1972). Once activated in the cell, these tobacco derivatives act as mutagens, exhibiting a linear dose-response tumorigenic effect (Andreasson et al 1984; Wynder and Hoffmann 1976).

In general the percentage of men with oral cancer is two to four times higher than that of women suffering from the same disease. In oral carcinoma the male-to-female ratio has been declining (reviewed in: Kleinman et al 1993). For a long time smoking and drinking was more common among men. In a delayed response to the growing number of female smokers, the death rate resulting from carcinomas of the upper aerodigestive tract in women has been increasing rapidly during the last three decades (Boring et al 1993). As with other head and neck cancers, OSCC is a disease of the elderly, with a peak incidence in the seventh decade, probably because of the duration and intensity of carcinogen exposure (Jovanovic et al

19

1993; Platz et al 1986). Less than 3% of cases involve patients younger than 40 years (Byers 1975; McGregor et al 1983).

Most cigarette-smoke-induced cancers in the upper aerodigestive tract occur in the larynx and lung, where the inhaled smoke is concentrated, and not in the oral cavity. In fact, heavy exposure to alcohol may be more closely correlated with oropharyngeal cancer (Dontenwill et al 1977; Schottenfeld 1979). The relative risk of developing a squamous cell carcinoma increases with the duration of the exposure to cigarette smoke and is not only increased but may be even potentiated by the concurrent use of alcohol (Tuyns et al 1977).

Although a number of epidemiologic and experimental studies have reconfirmed the correlation between alcohol consumption and oropharyngeal cancer, the mechanism of alcohol cocarcinogenesis remains unclear (Feldmann et al 1975; Graham et al 1977; Keller et al 1967; Maier et al 1990; Rothman and Keller 1972; Vincent and Marchetta 1963; Wynder et al 1957; Zöller et al 1992). Ethanol itself is not carcinogenic (Ketcham et al 1963). A direct topical effect of alcohol has been proposed because of the high correlation with carcinomas located in the upper digestive tract. Among the mechanisms that have been discussed for this local effect are the solvent properties of alcohol for carcinogens, a possible activation of procarcinogens due to enzyme induction, and a damaging effect on the epithelium leading to a higher uptake of carcinogens (Seitz et al 1984). At the same time ethanol-induced atrophy of salivary glands causes a reduction of saliva production, leading to an increase in concentration of carcinogenic substances in the saliva and a prolonged exposure of the epithelium to these substances. Poor oral hygiene has also been associated with development of carcinomas in the oral cavity, although this effect is much smaller than those of alcohol consumption and cigarette smoking (Marshall et al 1992). Because of a higher bacterial contamination, production of acetaldehyde from ethanol in these patients increases, which in turn damages the mucosa and leads to a more rapid proliferation of the oral epithelium (Pik-

karainen et al 1979; Mak et al 1987). Rapidly proliferating cells are more prone to DNA damage from mutagenic substances. A negative influence of ethanol on DNA repair has also been discussed. In addition the systemic effects of alcohol, dietary deficiencies, liver damage, and immunodeficiencies have also been indicated (Barch 1986; Graham et al 1977; Lieber et al 1986; Marshall et al 1992; Seitz and Simanowsky 1988; Wustrow and Issing 1993). A decrease in the number of antigen-presenting cells, eg, Langerhans cells, seems to be correlated with poor prognosis in carcinomas (Austyn 1993; Becker 1993; Girod et al 1994d; Kurihara and Hashimoto 1985; Nakashima et al 1992).

In the last decade the role of viral infections in head and neck squamous cell carcinoma, especially Epstein-Barr virus (EBV) and human papilloma virus (HPV), has been discussed. HPV infections are found in benign and malignant tumors of the upper aerodigestive tract, but the results remain controversial in head and neck cancer. HPV infection may lead to immortalization of mammalian cells, but alone is not sufficient to induce malignant transformation (Anderson et al 1994; Brachman et al 1992; Burns et al 1993; Cox et al 1993; de Villiers 1989; Gassenmaier 1988; Lee et al 1993; Lewensohn-Fuchs et al 1994; Milde-Lagnosch et al 1989; Miller et al 1994; Steinberg and Auborn 1993; Thomas et al 1994; Woods et al 1993).

Despite therapeutic and diagnostic advances, the prognosis of oropharyngeal squamous cell carcinoma remains poor and has not changed significantly during the last three decades (Platz et al 1988). To improve the control of locoregional recurrence and metastases, combination treatment including surgery, radiation therapy, and chemotherapy has been introduced into the treatment of OSCC. The planning of treatment and prognostic evaluation is largely based on the clinical TNM classification and recent studies confirmed that overall advanced T and N stage are the two parameters that significantly adversely affect survival in oral squamous cell carcinoma (Jones 1994). The TNM system is based on the assumption that small tumors without clinical spread have a better prognosis than larger tumors with local or distant metastases. Clinical experience shows, though, that individual tumors at the same stage of the disease may exhibit a completely different behavior with regard to growth potential, response to chemotherapy or radiotherapy, and the ability to metastasize. Careful statistical analysis of 3005 patients with oral cancer conducted by DÖSAK (German-Austrian-Swiss Association for Head and Neck Tumours; Hausamen 1988) revealed that the TNM-classification does not reflect the prognosis in some cases, because of the shortcomings attributed to the classification guidelines (Howaldt 1992). It is thus necessary to develop new methods to assess the prognostically relevant biological behavior of oral squamous cell carcinomas. Based on the results of this study, modification of the TNM-classification has been proposed. The DÖSAK cooperative group also developed an individual treatment-dependent prognostic index (TPI) to improve the prediction of a patient's individual prognosis (Platz et al 1986, 1988, 1992).

Histologic grading of the tumor differentiation is the most important supplement to clinical staging. Anneroth et al (1987) and Burkhardt (1985) reviewed previous works and redefined the grading criteria for OSCC. They recommended that the grading consist of six morphological features: degree of keratinization, nuclear polymorphism, number of mitoses, pattern of invasion, stage of invasion, and lymphoplasmatic infiltrate. Each feature is graded individually, a high sum of all scores indicating a poorer prognosis. Bryne (1989) found that the grading of the invasive front of the tumors is of higher prognostic significance than the grading of the entire tumor. Even the mode of invasion seems to be significant for the prognosis of individual tumors (Hell et al 1992; reviewed in: Carter 1993). The hypothesis that the invasive parts of the tumors may include more "aggressive" cells is also supported by immunohistochemical investigations using monoclonal antibodies against Ki-67 and proliferating cell nuclear antigen (PCNA). With these cell cycle-specific antibodies it has be-

come possible to assess the proliferation activity in tissue specimens by immunohistochemistry. Ki-67 as well as PCNA expression was often found to be increased in cells at the invasive front in OSCC, indicating a more rapid proliferation of the cells in this area (Edström et al 1991; Watling 1992). Maximum tumor thickness is another important reproducible and prognostically significant feature of histopathologic evaluation in OSCC (Borges et al 1989; Howaldt et al 1992; Nathanson and Agren 1989; Shingaki et al 1988; Spiro et al 1987; Urist et al 1987).

In recent years DNA content measurements in head and neck squamous cell carcinoma by flow cytometry and static cytometry have become possible. The widely used flow cytometry measures the amount of DNA in each cell of the investigated population by quantitating a fluorescent dye bound to the DNA. Though the results remain contradictory in OSCC, several studies have demonstrated correlations between the histologic grade, frequency of aneuploidy, and increasing percentage of cells in S phase associated with advanced clinical stage and poor patient outcomes (Böcking et al 1985; Borg et al 1992; Burgio et al 1992; Hemmer and Kreidler 1990; Kokal et al 1988; Nylander et al 1994; Suzuki et al 1994; Tytor et al 1990). Aneuploidy seems to gradually increase from premalignant lesions to OSCC (Borg 1992). Use of paraffin-embedded material for flow cytometry is now well documented, although limited numbers of tumor cells and large amounts of cell debris may alter the interpretability of the histograms. Differing characteristics among anatomic sites and a change of pattern from the primary tumor to the metastases have been demonstrated. Because cytometric techniques are still relatively time-consuming, their clinical usefulness is at present limited. Further research in this area should be of great benefit to clarify the changes during the process of tumor formation and development of metastases.

Cell-cell adhesion molecules such as E-cadherin have been shown to suppress invasive growth of epithelial cells in vitro, and loss of its expression is thought to be important in invasion and metastatic potential of epithelial tumors in vivo (Downer and Speight 1993; reviewed in: Hülsken et al 1994). A significant correlation between the level of membranous E-cadherin expression in the primary tumor and the degree of differentiation was found in head and neck tumors. E-cadherin expression also seems to have prognostic importance in patients with head and neck squamous cell carcinomas (HNSCC) (Mattijssen et al 1993; Schipper et al 1991). As E-cadherin has been shown to play a role in tissue specific retention of lymphocytes in the epithelium and mediate interaction of keratinocytes with Langerhans cells, the loss of expression in HNSCC might be related to an impaired immune response (Cepek et al 1994; Tang et al 1993). A number of other molecular and cellular features have been studied in premalignant and malignant oral lesions such as cytokeratins, filagrin, and involucrin (reviewed in: Bryne 1991). Multivariate analysis of several studies has not proven independent prognostic value for these markers.

2.2. Cell Growth Control, Tumor Suppressor Genes, and Epithelial Cancers

In general the biologic behavior of tumors can almost certainly be ascribed to compromised gene function resulting from genetic alterations that accumulate during the process of neoplastic transformation and tumor progression. If cancer were induced by a single genetic change that led to uncontrolled cell proliferation, theoretically thousands of different cancers would occur in a single person. In reality, malignant transformation is rare considering the number of cells at risk. Statistical analysis of the age correlated increase of cancer incidence suggests that the development of malignancy requires about five independent events (Cairns 1978).

The types of changes cancer cells and their precursors exhibit are point mutations, amplification of chromosomal regions, missing or extra chromosomes, and translocations. A special subset of genes involved in the control of the cell cycle seems to play a central role in the development of all human tumors regardless of the originating tissue. Oncogenes, the activated counterparts of proto-oncogenes, which are involved in the cell growth regulation of normal cells, promote unregulated cell proliferation. Tumor suppressor genes negatively regulate the cell cycle. Recent advances in the understanding of cell cycle control connect tumor suppressor genes with the regulation of cell cycle promotion at the transition step to DNA synthesis in the mammalian cell cycle, where mitogenic and antiproliferative signals are integrated. The interactions of tumor suppressor genes with the cell cycle machinery and the resulting effects on the control of cell proliferation and differentiation bring to light some of the important mechanisms of oncogenesis.

The survival of cells and thus organisms depends on their ability to accurately transmit their genetic information. Failure to complete DNA replication and to repair DNA damage results in the propagation of genetic mutations that may result in the development of unrestricted growth as it is observed in OSCC. To ensure the production of healthy progeny, cells employ two types of mechanisms. Either cell cycle progression is delayed at cell cycle checkpoints until the DNA damage has been repaired or cells undergo deliberately induced cell death, called apoptosis. Although some cells die, production of malignant clones is avoided. The failure of cells to arrest, or apoptose, has been related to inactivation of tumor suppressor genes by several mechanisms, such as the action of tumor viruses. Genetic alterations are therefore further accumulated in these cells and promote and help sustain malignant transformation.

2.2.1. Cell Cycle Regulation and Oral Carcinogenesis

Oral squamous cell carcinoma cells, like any other cancer cells, can overcome the normal strictures against unlimited proliferation and metastases and display a variety of genetic changes. Recent results explain how the loss of checkpoint control during the cell cycle due to inactivation of cell cycle inhibitors or overexpression of cell cycle promoters may lead to the uncontrolled cell cycle progression that can be observed in malignant tumors.

A cell divides into two daughter cells by progressing serially through four precisely controlled phases of the cell cycle: G1, in which the cells begin to grow, followed by S phase, when DNA synthesis occurs; a second growth phase G2; and finally mitosis (M) (Murray and Hunt 1993; reviewed in: Reddy 1994). Cells deprived of nutrients withdraw from the cell cycle and arrest in early G1 phase in a quiescent state (G0). DNA content varies according to the cell cycle stage. As discussed in chapter 2.1.2., the amount of DNA in a cell can be assessed using flow cytometry, which has also been widely used as a diagnostic tool in head and neck squamous cell carcinoma. G2 cells have exactly twice the amount of the DNA of G1 cells. Cells in S phase have an intermediate amount of DNA.

The length of the cell cycle in mammalian cells varies greatly. In rapidly dividing human cells, such as the epithelial precursor cells in the oral mucosa, the cell cycle lasts about 24 hours. However, not all cells in the organism replicate continuously. Differentiated mammalian cells leave the cell cycle transiently after cell division. Thus most cells in the human body are non-proliferating cells in G0. If terminal differentiation occurs, cells even irreversibly withdraw from the cell cycle. In the normal oral epithelium only the cells located in the basal cell membrane proliferate. They then move up toward the surface of the epithelium while they differentiate, thus constantly renewing the protective epithelial lineage of the oropharynx.

Transition between different stages of the cell cycle is regulated at checkpoints (reviewed in: Murray 1994). In mammalian cells the "restriction point" in late G1 is the major and currently best understood checkpoint, where the progress of the cell cycle is coordinated. Depending on positive or negative external and internal signals, the cell commits itself irreversibly to DNA replication. After the decision for DNA synthesis has been made, the cells are refractory to growth factor-induced signals. Progression through mitosis seems to be regulated exclusively by internal mechanisms (Pardee 1989). Deregulation of cell cycle progression occurs at the cell cycle checkpoints as a result of either aberrant expression of positive regulators or impaired function of negative regulators that may result in uninhibited cell growth. Studies of human cells in tissue culture have revealed two classes of genes that are involved in the deregulation of cell proliferation: oncogenes and tumor suppressor genes. Both types of changes have been documented in a wide variety of human tumor cells, including cells originating from oral epithelium.

Most oncogenes are components of the signaling pathway, such as growth factors, growth factor receptors, second messenger proteins, protein kinases and early and delayed response genes. In contrast to their normal cellular counterparts the proto-oncogenes, oncogenes stimulate cell growth independently and allow cells to escape from the normal controls of cell proliferation. In head and neck cancer, including OSCC, a wide range of oncogenic changes can be found during tumorigenesis. Conversely, tumor suppressor genes inhibit cell growth. Recessive mutations can inactivate these genes, again leading to unrestrained cell growth and inactivation of controls that allow growth arrest for repair of DNA damage.

Promoters of Mammalian Cell Proliferation

Cell proliferation is regulated by a chain of events that usually begins with the interaction of growth factors and their receptors. Growth factors activate their receptors, inducing second messengers, which in turn stimulate mainly protein kinases and phosphatases. Changes in protein phosphorylation then lead to the transcription of early response genes that encode transcription factors, which induce transcription of delayed response genes such as cyclins in the G1 phase of the cell cycle. Cyclin-cdk (cyclin-dependent kinases) complexes then inactivate negative regulator gene products, eg, tumor suppressor genes, thus allowing the cells to pass through the restriction point.

In mammalian cells and thus epithelial cells, progression through the cell cycle is thought to be the result of sequential activation of cyclin-dependent kinases by complexing with specific cyclins. The cyclin-cdk complexes most closely linked to the regulation of the restriction point at G1-S in these cells are the D-type cyclins and their partner cdks, preferentially cdk4 and cdk6 (reviewed in: Sherr 1993, 1994). There are three partially cell type-specific types of D cyclins: D1/PRAD1, D2, and D3 (Motokura et al 1991; Xiong et al 1992a, 1992b; Matsushime et al 1991). The expression of the D-type cyclins is inducible by growth factors, and the resulting activation of the cdks, mostly either cdk4 or cdk6, drives cells through the G1/S restriction point (Ajchenbaum et al 1993; Matsushime et al 1991; Winston and Pledger 1993; Won et al 1992).

Deregulation of cyclin D1 synthesis may render cells independent from growth factor stimulation and may thus indirectly contribute to the malignant phenotype (reviewed in: Motokura and Arnold 1993). By giving the impression of constant presence of growth factors, the cell cycle machinery is driven to continue through the cell cycle rather than differentiate. In fact, the cyclin D1 was found to be identical with the PRAD1 proto-oncogene which is overexpressed in benign parathyroid tumors (Motokura et al 1991). However, cyclin D1 overexpression alone is insufficient to transform primary cells; rather it has been shown to cooperate with known oncogenes such as ras and myc (Bodrug et al 1994; Hinds et al 1994; Lovec et al 1994a, 1994b). Nevertheless, in mouse experiments cyclin D1 overexpression led to mammary hyperplasia and carcinomas (Wang et al 1994a). Since cyclin D1 is essential for the passage through the G1-S restriction

point, it has been hypothesized that overexpression of cyclin D1 may play a role not only in the establishment of the malignant phenotype, but also in its maintenance (Lukas et al 1994a, 1994b). Not surprisingly, overexpression of cyclin D1 has been demonstrated in a wide range of squamous cell carcinomas, including breast, stomach, lung, and esophageal tumors, and most recently in head and neck carcinomas (Buckley et al 1993; Callender et al 1994; Jiang et al 1993; Jares et al 1994; Lammie et al 1991; Rosenberg et al 1993; Schauer et al 1994; Schuuring et al 1992; Tsuruta et al 1993; Wu et al 1994). Cyclin D1 overexpression seems to contribute not only to the proliferation of certain cell types, but also to the development of malignant tumors. Similarly, cyclin D2 gene amplification was found in colorectal tumors. No such findings have been reported for cyclin D3 yet (Leach et al 1993).

If D-type cyclins play a role in the establishment of the malignant transformation it can be expected that their main partner, cdk4, may also be involved in oncogenesis. Indeed, when quiescent cells are stimulated with mitogens, cdk4 expression is induced (Matsushime et al 1991). Cdk4 overexpression or amplification has been found in human tumor cell lines and tumors (Khatib et al 1993). Cdk4 may also be the target for TGF-β (transforming growth factor β) induced growth arrest in some cells, eg, human keratinocytes, and overexpression of cdk4 may render cells resistant to TGF-β mediated growth arrest. In differentiating cells, cdk4 is rapidly downregulated, whereas constitutively expressed cdk4 prevents differentiation, suggesting that cdk4 plays a role in cell differentiation (Kiyokawa et al 1994).

Cyclins E and A are thought to be functioning sequentially after the D-type cyclins during the cell cycle at the G1-S transition. They activate cdk2, which is believed to be involved in the initiation of DNA replication (Fang and Newport 1991; Koff et al 1991). Overexpression of cyclin E in mammalian fibroblasts causes premature DNA synthesis, while antibody injection against cyclin A or E blocks entry into S phase (Girard et al 1991; Ohtsubo and Roberts 1993). Cyclin E overexpression has been found in human tumors and cell lines, although its onco-genic potential is yet unclear (Buckley et al 1993; Keyomarsi et al 1994; Keyomarsi and Pardee 1993; Khatib et al 1993; Leach et al 1993; Sewing et al 1994). The role of cyclin A in malignant transformation was discovered early in HBV-related hepatoma (reviewed in: Brechot 1993). In hematologic malignancies, cyclin A expression correlated well with the pro-liferation rate of the malignant clones (Paterlini et al 1993). Both cyclin E and A interact with p107, a related protein of the retinoblastoma gene, and the transcription factor E2F and may thereby also participate in oncogenesis. Cyclin E first stimulates and cyclin A then inhibits the E2F-dependent transcription of genes later in the cycle (Devoto et al 1992; Dynlacht et al 1994; Ewen et al 1992; Faha et al 1992; Krek et al 1994; Lees et al 1992). However, the pres-ence of an intact retinoblastoma protein is not required for cyclin A function in cell cycle reg-ulation (Henglein et al 1994).

Inhibitors of Mammalian Cell Proliferation

Recently cdk-inhibitors of the mammalian cell cycle progression have been identified that act as potential tumor suppressors (reviewed in: Hunter and Pines 1994; Elledge and Harper 1994). Control of the G1-S transition in mam-malian cells may be influenced by a family of cdk-inhibitors that include the recently de-scribed inhibitors p21, p27, the Ink-protein fam-ily and a new protein p28 (Hengst et al 1994). As different cdk-inhibitors target the same ki-nases, different regulatory cycles seem to be involved. Loss of cdk-inhibitor function should be another mechanism by which cells can lose their growth control and exhibit the unre-strained proliferation that is typical of malignant cells.

A protein known as p21, also known as SDI1, WAF1, CIP1, CAP20, or PIC1, is currently the best-studied cdk-inhibitor, and there is strong evidence for the role of p21 in cellular trans-formation. Among others, p21 was detected by different laboratories as a gene induced by p53 (WAF1) and preventing senescent cells from entering the cell cycle (SDI1) (El-Deiry et al 1993; Noda et al 1994). This protein is a uni-versal cdk-inhibitor, binding to a wide variety of cyclin-cdk complexes including cyclin D-cdk4, cyclin E-cdk2, and cyclin A-cdk2. These com-plexes play an important role in the regulation of the G1-S restriction point and DNA replica-tion (reviewed in: Sherr 1993, 1994).

Expression of p21 is induced by the wild-type form of the p53 tumor suppressor gene and seems to be essential in mediating p53 in-duced growth arrest in the cell cycle in re-sponse to DNA damage (Dulic et al 1994; El-Deiry et al 1993,1994; Xiong et al 1993a, 1993b). The level of p21 mRNA and the inter-action of p21 protein with cyclin-cdk enzymes are regulated during the cell cycle. Whereas the expression of most cyclin-cdk-p21 com-plexes oscillates during the cell cycle, cyclin D1-cdk4-p21 complexes persist, suggesting that cyclin D1-cdk4 complexes may play a role in monitoring events that may occur at any time, rather than at a specific stage of the cell cycle (Li et al 1994a, 1994b). In transformed cells the p21 level is generally low, possibly due to lack of p53 stimulation (El-Deiry et al 1993,1994; Xiong et al 1992a, 1992b). Be-cause p21 expression can also be induced in cells that do not contain p53, it is likely that other regulatory pathways of p21 exist (Michieli et al 1994).

Another protein with partial sequence identity with p21, p27, also inhibits cdks (Polyak et al 1994a, 1994b; Toyoshima and Hunter 1994). p27 was detected as part of a cyclin E-cdk2 complex that was identified in TGF-β treated, cell cycle-arrested epithelial cells (Polyak et al 1994a, 1994b). p21 and p27 levels change re-ciprocally during the cell cycle (Firpo et al 1994; Kato et al 1994; Slingerland et al 1994). p27 is elevated in quiescent cells, and when cells enter the cell cycle, p27 is titrated by cyclin D-cdk4 complexes. TGF-β has been shown to in-hibit cdk4 synthesis, leading to a reduction of cyclin D-cdk4 complexes and freeing p27. The level of p27 thus rises in the cells, inhibiting cy-clin E-cdk2 complexes and inducing G1 arrest (Koff et al 1993; Polyak et al 1994a, 1994b). In-activation of p27 may promote cyclin E-cdk2

25

kinase activity, thus establishing their order of action of cyclin-cdk complexes.

Another candidate cdk-inhibitor with tumor suppressor functions is the p16[ink4] protein. The Ink4 proteins represent a family of proteins that selectively inhibit certain cdks (Serrano et al 1993; reviewed in: Sherr 1993, 1994). p16[ink4] was identified as an inhibitor of cdk4 and cdk6, thus competing with the D cyclins (Hannon and Beach 1994; Serrano et al 1993). In Rb negative cells p16[ink4] is upregulated and associates with cdk4 at the expense of cyclin D, suggesting that Rb may repress p16[ink4] expression (Li et al 1994a, 1994b). Cdk4 is no longer required for cell cycle progression in these cells (Lukas et al 1994a, 1994b). It has been hypothesized that p16[ink4] expression may be regulated by Rb-related transcription factors, thus functioning in a feedback loop to inhibit cdk4 action after the growth suppressive function of Rb is canceled. p16[ink4] is related to the MTS1 tumor suppressor gene, a gene involved in familial predisposition for malignant melanomas (MLM) which maps to the same region of chromosome 9 (Nobori et al 1994). p16[ink4] mutations have also been found in some primary tumors, among them esophageal squamous cell carcinomas (Mori et al 1994).

Another member of the Ink4 family is a protein called p15[ink4], which is suspected to be the MTS2 tumor suppressor gene. p15[ink4] lies close to p16 on the same chromosome. In human keratinocytes p15[ink4] expression is increased after treatment with TGF-β, suggesting that p15[ink4] mediates growth arrest in these cells, by binding and inactivating cdk4 and cdk6 (Hannon and Beach 1994). Two more related proteins, p15.5[ink4] and p18[ink4], are also excellent candidates for a family of G1 cdk-inhibitor tumor suppressor genes, although further studies have to be performed (Guan et al 1994; Hannon and Beach 1994).

2.2.2. Tumor Suppressor Gene Functions and Dysfunctions

Loss of tumor suppressor gene function and thus of regulation of cell proliferation function is an important factor in cancer development. The role of the tumor suppressor genes Rb and p53 is well characterized in the mammalian cell cycle control. Their inactivation occurs mostly either as a result of mutations or deletions, or through binding to cellular regulatory proteins or viral oncogenes, or, in the case of p53, through interaction with the mdm2 (murine-double-minute) gene. Impairment of function of p53 and Rb has been found in a wide variety of human cancers. In fact, p53 changes are believed to be the most frequent alterations occurring in human tumorigenesis. Impairment of function of these genes due to the outlined mechanisms also seems to play a major role in oral carcinogenesis and has important implications for the prognosis and therapy of the OSCC and its precursors in the future.

The Retinoblastoma Tumor Suppressor Gene

Retinoblastoma is a childhood cancer that occurs in hereditary and nonhereditary forms. Knudson (1971) developed the hypothesis that two mutational events were necessary to cause this malignancy. Subsequently the retinoblastoma (Rb) gene was localized to the 13q14 chromosomal region, and in tumor cells of retinoblastomas a frequent development of homozygosity for the mutant allele of the Rb gene was found (Benedict et al 1983; Cavenee et al 1983; Dryja et al 1984; Godbout et al 1983; Yunis and Ramsay 1978). A few years later the gene was isolated by molecular cloning (Friend et al 1986, reviewed in: Weinberg 1992).

Rb is a prototype tumor suppressor gene. The gene encodes an approximately 105 to 110kd nuclear phosphoprotein found primarily in the nucleus of all mammalian cells and human tissues tested so far, including the epithelium of the gastrointestinal tract (Cordon-Cardo and Richon 1994; Friend et al 1987; Lee et al 1987).

Retinoblastoma tumor cells fail to express a functional Rb protein due to mutation of the gene (Horowitz et al 1989; Lee et al 1987; Whyte et al 1988). A mutated form of the gene can be detected not only in retinoblastomas but also in a wide range of human tumors, eg, breast carcinomas, small cell lung cancer, osteosarcomas (Cheng et al 1990; Friend et al 1987; Fung et al 1987; Hensel et al 1990; Harbour et al 1988; Lee et al 1988; Lundberg et al 1987; Shew et al 1989; T'Ang et al 1988; Varley et al 1989; Yokota et al 1987).

Animal studies in knockout mice in which the Rb gene has been inactivated have shown that Rb is an essential gene in mouse development. Embryos homozygous for the mutation (Rb$^-$/Rb$^-$) die between days 14 and 15 of gestation showing defects of the hematopoetic and nervous systems (Jacks et al 1992; Lee et al 1992). Surprisingly, heterozygous animals are not predisposed to retinoblastoma, but in some cases display pituitary tumors. In the homozygous mice, loss of function of both alleles of the Rb gene deregulates cell proliferation in the lens, permitting cellular DNA synthesis during terminal differentiation of the cells. At the same time a p53-dependent program is activated that leads to apoptosis of these cells (Morgenbesser et al 1994; Pan and Griep 1994). Conversely, introduction of a normal Rb gene into retinoblastoma cells or other cells containing a mutated Rb gene in vitro partially reverts the neoplastic phenotype, and either slows down the growth rate in some cell types or inhibits progression into S phase (Goodrich et al 1991). Most importantly, tumorigenicity of the transfected cells in nude mice is lost, thus demonstrating the tumor suppressor function of Rb (Bookstein et al 1990; Huang et al 1988).

The Rb phosphoprotein is synthesized throughout the cell cycle, but the phosphorylation pattern changes in a cell cycle-dependent manner. In resting cells (G0) and early G1, Rb is underphosphorylated, whereas in rapidly proliferating cells in S and G2, Rb is highly phosphorylated (Buchkovich et al 1989; Chen et al 1989; DeCaprio et al 1989; Ludlow et al 1989, 1990; Mihara et al 1989; Xu et al 1989). Phosphorylation of Rb occurs at the G1-S boundary, indicating that Rb phosphorylation plays an important role in overcoming the restriction point in mammalian cells that dedicates them to proliferation. This view has been supported early on by the observation that underphosphorylated Rb forms stable complexes with viral transforming proteins, including SV 40 large T antigen, E1A of human adenovirus 5, and the E7 protein of HPV-16 and -18.

The DNA tumor viruses target and disrupt Rb cyclin-p107-E2F associated complexes releasing E2F, which in turn activates transcription of its related genes. This mechanism may lead to immortalization of mammalian cells infected with these viruses and contribute to the development of the malignant phenotype in OSCC (Bandara et al 1993; Barbosa et al 1990; DeCaprio et al 1988; Dyson 1989; Johnson et al 1993; Münger et al 1989; Singh et al 1994; Whyte et al 1988; Nevins 1994). The binding domain of Rb to the viral proteins has been identified, and it seems that most mutations in the Rb gene occur in this region (Hu et al 1990; Kaelin et al 1990). These results suggest that the growth inhibitory effect of Rb can be overcome either by phosphorylation or by binding to a tumor virus protein (Ludlow et al 1989, 1990).

In fact, during G0 and G1 the unphosphorylated Rb protein forms stable complexes with DNA-binding proteins, eg, members of the E2F family of transcription factors (reviewed in: Nevins 1992). By binding to these proteins and thus inhibiting their activity, Rb exerts its negative regulatory effect on gene expression and cell cycle progression at the G1-S restriction point. When Rb is phosphorylated, the transcription factor E2F is released from the complex, allowing the activation of gene transcription necessary for traversing the G1/S restriction point. Rb phosphorylation is indirectly regulated by p53 and the cdk-inhibitor p21. It only occurs if the cell's genomic integrity is established, and it is thus ready to proceed in the cell cycle. Among others, E2F sites are present in the promoters of genes encoding thymidine kinase, Myc, Myb, dihydrofolate reductase, and DNA polymerase α, the products of which play a role in the induction of S phase.

Rb can be phosphorylated and thus inactivated in vitro by several D-type cyclins, but not all D-type cyclins function equivalently (Ewen et al 1993). Reversion of the cycle-blocking function of Rb seems to be the almost exclusive role of cyclin D1 (reviewed in: Hunter and Pines 1994). In cells lacking functional Rb, cyclin D1 and cyclin D1-cdk4 complexes are downregulated. Conversely, exogenously expressed Rb induces cyclin D1, suggesting an autoregulatory feedback loop mechanism that regulates both the expression of the cyclin D1 gene and the activity of pRb, thereby contributing to a G1 phase checkpoint control in cycling mammalian cells. In addition cyclin D1 is dispensable for passage through the cell cycle in cell lines whose pRb is inactivated through complex formation with T antigen, E1A, or E7 oncoproteins (Lukas et al 1994a, 1994b; Müller et al 1994). Thus the connection between D-type cyclins and tumorigenesis is strengthened further.

Rb and D-type cyclins not only play an important role in the control of cell proliferation, they also seem to regulate the switch between cell division and cell differentiation by binding to different factors. After treatment of cells with retinoic acid, dephosphorylation of Rb appears as a relatively late-occurring component of the metabolic cascade culminating in G0-arrested, phenotypically differentiated cells and inhibiting the release of cell cycle promoters such as E2F. Hypophosphorylated Rb does not seem to play a role in initiating, but rather in sustaining the differentiated state (Chen et al 1989; reviewed in: Hollingsworth et al 1993; Yen and Varvayanis 1994). Phosphorylation of Rb again relieves this inhibition (reviewed in: Hinds and Weinberg 1994). Ectopical expression of cyclins also prevents cells from differentiating and they then proliferate until they die (Kato and Sherr 1993).

Constitutively expressed cyclins A and E can also overcome Rb-mediated suppression of proliferation. Rb becomes hyperphosphorylated in cells overexpressing these cyclins, and this phosphorylation is essential for cyclin A- and cyclin E-mediated rescue of pRb-blocked cells. This suggests that G1 and S phase cyclins can act as regulators of pRb function in the cell cycle by promoting pRb phosphorylation (Hinds et al 1992).

The p53 Tumor Suppressor Gene

Nearly all human cancers are associated with a loss of function of the p53 tumor suppressor gene, indicating the important role of p53 in cancer development (Hollstein et al 1991, 1994a). Inactivation of the gene is mostly due to missense mutations, but it can also be caused by a variety of other mechanisms, including deletions, interactions with oncogenic viral or cellular proteins and possibly intracellular translocation from the nucleus to the cytoplasm, where the protein is inactive (Mietz et al 1992; Moll et al 1992; Momand et al 1992; Nigro et al 1989; Shaulsky et al 1991). The major function of p53 is cell cycle arrest in G1 phase in response to DNA damage, allowing for DNA repair and the regulation of programmed cell death (apoptosis). p53 presumably acts to protect cells against the accumulation of mutations and subsequent conversion to a cancerous state. Thus, the role of p53 in suppressing tumorigenesis may be to rescue the cell or organism from the mutagenic effects of DNA damage. Although p53 is not required in normal cell growth, its action as a tumor suppressor becomes critical in the event of cellular stress and DNA damage.

Normal cells containing a functional p53 exhibit regular cell growth control, while cells lacking p53 have lost this cell cycle control and presumably accumulate damage-induced mutations that result in malignant transformation of cells (reviewed in: Lane 1992; Mercer and Baserga 1991; Oren 1992; Perry and Levine 1993; Vogelstein and Kinzler 1992). In quiescent cells and immortal cells in culture the p53 level is low and increases upon the entry of the cells into the cell cycle (Mercer and Baserga 1991; Reich and Levine 1984). In mammalian cells p53 is essential in the delay of the cell cycle at the G1 restriction point. Following γ-irradiation, mammalian cells with wild-type p53 exhibit transient G1 and G2 arrest. Tumor cell lines, including those derived from HNSCC with mutations of the p53 gene that inactivate the gene or lead to overexpression of abnormal protein, do not display the same feedback control in G1. Cells can initiate DNA replication and continue through the G1-S restriction point, but p53 inactivation does not influence the feedback control in G2 (Kastan et al 1991). Introduction of wild-type p53 into the malignant cells partially restores G1 arrest (Brenner et al 1993; Kuerbitz et al 1992; Liu et al 1994). It therefore appears that p53 plays an important role in G1 arrest but not in G2.

The mechanisms of p53 action have only recently been further elucidated by studies in p53 knockout mice and cell lines lacking a functional p53 gene. p53 homozygous knockout mice are viable, but they develop a wide range of malignancies at an early age. Heterozygous mice (p53$^+$/p53$^-$) display a tumor spectrum similar to that of Li-Fraumeni patients who carry the same genotype (Birch et al 1994). Furthermore, in vivo and in vitro studies showed that thymocytes of p53 deficient mice were resistant to the lethal effects of γ-irradiation, whereas cells with a heterozygous genotype (p53$^+$/p53$^-$) displayed intermediate viability (Clarke et al 1993; Lowe et al 1993b).

Normally p53 is able to mediate cell growth arrest in response to DNA damage to allow for DNA repair or trigger apoptosis, thus helping to ensure genetic stability (Diller et al 1990; Kastan et al 1991; Livingstone et al 1992). Both the level of the protein and its transcriptional transactivation activity increase following treatment of cells with agents that damage DNA. Overexpression of the wild-type p53 protein results either in arrest in the G1 phase of the cell cycle or in the induction of apoptosis (Martinez et al 1991; Ullrich et al 1992; Yonish-Rouach et al 1991). In differentiating cells in cell culture the level of p53 decreases (Dony et al 1985; Oren et al 1982; Rogel et al 1985; Shen et al 1983). In OSCC cell lines, transfection of wild-type p53 did not restore responsiveness of cells to growth inhibition in all lines, but the cells did re-express proteins that appear typically during squamous cell differentiation. Some cell lines showed cell morphological changes consistent with apoptosis. In vivo studies in nude mice with established squamous carcinoma nodules showed that tumor volumes were significantly reduced in mice that received peritumoral infiltration of p53 (Brenner et al 1993; Liu et al 1994).

p53 exerts its functions by binding to DNA in a sequence-specific binding manner that seems to be essential for its action as a tumor suppressor (Pietenpol et al 1994). The gene contains a strong transactivational sequence at its amino-terminus, thus acting as a transcription factor, stimulating the expression of genes downstream of its binding site in mammalian cells (Funk et al 1992; Kern et al 1991,1992; Zambetti et al 1992). Among the genes whose transcription is p53 dependent are the universal cdk-inhibitor p21 and a 90kd protein named MDM2. Both proteins are important in cell growth control in mammalian cells (Barak et al 1993; El-Deiry et al 1993; Harper et al 1993; Wu et al 1993; Xiong et al 1993a, 1993b). p53 also negatively regulates a variety of genes that do not contain a p53- responsive element (Seto et al 1992).

In situations where the genomic integrity of the cell is threatened and p53 accumulates in a transcriptionally active form, it induces the expression p21 (DiLeonardo et al 1994; Dulic et al 1994; El-Deiry et al 1993; Harper et al 1993; Lu and Lane 1993; Noda et al 1994; Xiong et al 1993a, 1993b). p21 then inhibits the kinase activity of multiple cdk-complexes, thus blocking Rb phosphorylation and consequently E2F release, which results in cellular growth suppression (reviewed in: Hollingsworth et al 1993; Slebos et al 1994; reviewed in: Sherr 1993, 1994).

Recently p21 was found to bind to proliferating nuclear antigen (PCNA), an auxiliary protein of DNA polymerase δ, the principal replicative DNA polymerase. p21 inhibits PCNA-dependent DNA replication in the absence of a cyclin/cdk and blocks the ability of PCNA to activate DNA polymerase δ. This regulation results from a direct interaction between p21 and PCNA (Flores-Rozas et al 1994; Waga et al 1994). Because p21 is a target of the tumor suppressor gene p53, p21 and PCNA are important for the coordinating of cell-cycle progression, DNA replication, and therefore repair of damaged DNA during p53-mediated suppression of cell proliferation. After DNA damage, p21 is induced following p53 induction. By inactivating cdk activity via p21, p53 indirectly prevents the phosphorylation of the retinoblastoma protein and thus the release of the E2F transcription factor.

PCNA plays an important role in DNA replication and repair during the cell cycle. Serum of patients with systemic lupus erythematodes reacted with nuclei of proliferating cells in normal human tissues. PCNA-specific antibodies were found to inhibit DNA synthesis, and PCNA antigen oligodesoxynucleotides were able to inhibit proliferation of Balb/c3T3 fibroblasts, indicating the importance of the protein for DNA replication (Jasulski et al 1988; Wong et al 1987). PCNA was identified as a 36kd nuclear protein required for leading-strand DNA synthesis by polymerase δ and nucleotide excision repair (Almendral et al 1987; Bravo et al 1987; Henderson et al 1994; Shivji et al 1992; van Vuuren et al 1993). Because of its cell cycle-dependent expression, detection of the protein has been used widely for the determination of the proliferation status of paraffin-embedded tissue specimens by immunohistochemistry. Further research identified PCNA as a component of multiple cyclin-cdk complexes in normal cells (Matsuoka et al 1994; Xiong et al 1992a, 1992b, 1993a, 1993b; Zhang et al 1993).

Several genes have been identified that further mediate the role of p53 as a tumor suppressor, among them GADD45, a gene induced by DNA damage ("growth-arrest-and-DNA-damage inducible"). GADD45 is inducible not only by wild-type p53 but also by p21 (Fornace et al 1992; Kastan et al 1992). Furthermore GADD45 complexes with proliferating cell nuclear antigen (PCNA) in response to DNA damage (Smith et al 1994). In interacting with PCNA, GADD45 stimulates DNA repair by an, as yet, unknown mechanism. Thus p53 is able to indirectly influence DNA repair by acting through GADD45 and halting DNA synthesis through p21 (Li et al 1994a, 1994b; Waga et al 1994). p21 seems

to efficiently inhibit synthesis of long but not short templates, suggesting that its association with PCNA is likely to impair the progressive movement of polymerase δ during DNA chain elongation, thus allowing DNA repair, but not synthesis of long DNA stretches (Flores-Rozas et al 1994). Recently it has been shown that p53 may also stimulate DNA repair more directly by interacting with the excision repair molecule ERCC3 (Wang et al 1994b).

The transcriptional activity of p53 can also be abrogated by its binding to viral oncoproteins such as E1B of the human adenovirus, HPV E6, and SV40 large T antigen (Mietz et al 1992; Sarnow et al 1982). The oncogenic products of these DNA tumor viruses inhibit the ability of p53 to bind to DNA and act as a transcription factor, thus allowing the transformation of cells that do not allow viral replication (Farmer et al 1992; Mietz et al 1992; Yew and Berk 1992). DNA tumor viruses thus circumvent the control mechanisms of the cell cycle by inactivating p53 as well as the retinoblastoma protein. This mechanism only seems to play a role in a subset of HNSCC (Burns et al 1993; Thomas et al 1994).

Another cellular protein, p90 or p95, was also found to bind to both mutant and wild-type p53 and was identified as the previously known MDM2 oncogene (Momand et al 1992; Wu et al 1993). MDM2 was first detected as an amplified gene in a tumorigenic cell line derived from mouse fibroblasts (Fakharazadeh et al 1991). Following irradiation MDM2 is induced in cells containing a wild-type but not a mutant p53 gene, suggesting that transcription of MDM2 depends on p53 (Juven et al 1993; Perry et al 1993; Price and Park 1994). Excess MDM2 can then bind to p53 and abrogate the transcriptional activation function of p53 again (Brown et al 1993). Overexpression of MDM2 may serve as a negative regulator of p53 function in late G1 phase, bypassing the need for structural alteration of the protein and leading to unrestricted cell growth and malignant transformation in cooperation with known oncogenes (Chen et al 1994; Finlay 1993; Olson et al 1993). These observations demonstrate that MDM2 overexpression can inhibit the p53 functional pathway and are consistent with the hypothesis that MDM2 may function in a "feedback loop" mechanism with p53, possibly acting to limit the length or severity of the p53-mediated arrest following DNA damage (Wu et al 1993; reviewed in: Picksley and Lane 1993). Recent analysis has identified the MDM2 binding site to be a short stretch within the amino-terminal domain of the p53 gene (Picksley and Lane 1994). Mutational analysis suggests that the target sites are partially overlapping, which is how MDM2 binding can interrupt the transcriptional activation function of p53. Enhanced levels of the gene are found in p53 growth-arrested cell lines (Barak et al 1993; Momand et al 1992).

Since then MDM2 overexpression has been found in tumors and cell lines deriving from sarcomas and gliomas from which p53 mutations were often absent (Cordon-Cardo et al 1994; Khatib et al 1993; Leach et al 1993; Oliner et al 1992; Reifenberger et al 1993). Inactivation of the p53 gene due to MDM2 overexpression may play an important role in the development of malignancy in these cases (Ladanyi et al 1993; Oliner et al 1992). MDM2 amplification was not detected in tumors of the upper aerodigestive tract, where p53 mutation is frequent, although by immunohistochemistry MDM2 staining was found in a high percentage of benign and malignant lung tissue specimens (Waber et al 1993; Wiethege et al 1994). In hematologic and lymphoid malignancies, malignant melanoma, Ewing's sarcoma, and angiosarcoma, as well as esophageal carcinomas, MDM2 amplification was not found to be an important mechanism of p53 inactivation (Cesarman et al 1994; Esteve et al 1993; Florenes et al 1994; Hollstein et al 1994a, 1994b; Kovar et al 1993; Preudhomme et al 1993).

Arrest of cell cycle progression can occur at any point during the cell cycle. Cancer cells display defects at the G1-S, as well as at the G2-M checkpoints and at the end of metaphase, when spindles are formed. Only recently have studies in p53 and/or Rb knockout mice and deficient cell lines revealed important information about the cooperation of these tumor suppressor genes to ensure the genetic integrity of proliferating mammalian cells and thus the survival of the organism (reviewed in: Picksley and Lane 1994). Because the tumor suppressor protein p53 appears to function at the G1 phase of the cell cycle as a checkpoint in response to DNA damage, mutations in the p53 gene lead to an increased rate of genomic instability and tumorigenesis. If p53 fails to arrest cell cycle progression after DNA damage, not only unrestricted cell proliferation may result, but also the propagation of DNA damage to the descendant cells. This could contribute to the increased incidence of chromosomal abnormalities and genetic instability that can be observed in tumor cells (reviewed in: Hartwell 1992). Loss of function of both alleles of the Rb gene also deregulates cell proliferation, permitting cellular DNA synthesis during terminal differentiation of cells. At the same, time a p53-dependent program is activated that leads to the efficient elimination of these cells (Morgenbesser et al 1994; Pan and Griep 1994). In mouse experiments p53 counteracts uncontrolled proliferation that accompanies loss of Rb (White 1994). These studies provide evidence that p53 may in fact act as a tumor suppressor by eliminating premalignant cells, which may eventually show malignant transformation and thus endanger the organism. Furthermore the tumor suppressor genes Rb and p53 interact in the cell cycle and seem to compensate for each other's loss of function in response to DNA damage. Rb regulates the passage of G1-S by controlling the E2F transcription factor, whereas p53 activates p21 thus inhibiting several cell cycle-dependent kinases and cell cycle progression. Coexpression of the wild-type p53 protein and E2F in mammalian cells resulted in a rapid loss of cell viability through a process of apoptosis. Thus, the cell cycle utilizes an interacting or communicative pathway between Rb-E2F and p53 (Wu and Levine 1994). Therefore, as long as Rb function is intact, p53 function may not be apparent. In the event Rb function is lost, p53 may inhibit cell cycle progression.

3. Material and Methods

3.1. Tissue Specimens of Lichen Planus, Leukoplakia, and Oral Squamous Cell Carcinomas and Histologic Classification

3.1.1. Collection of Material

Paraffin Embedded Tissue

In patients who present with oral lichen planus, oral leukoplakia and oral squamous cell carcinoma at the Department of Oral and Maxillofacial Surgery, University of Cologne, biopsy specimens are taken if malignant transformation is suspected in the benign lesions or if the diagnosis has to be established by histopathology prior to treatment of the tumors. Biopsy tissue from 113 patients with oral lichen planus and oral leukoplakia who presented from 1974 until 1992 was available for further analysis. From 1986 until 1991, 144 patients with OSCC were treated with a standardized protocol to evaluate the effects of preoperative radiochemotherapy. In all patients biopsy specimens were taken prior to therapy. The treatment regimen consisted of locoregional radiotherapy (39.6 Gy) and simultaneous infusion of Cisplatinum on days 1 to 5 (20 mg/m^2 body surface), followed by radical en-bloc surgery of the primary tumor and the cervical lymph nodes. If the tumor margins were positive after surgery and in cases with extracapsular lymph node extension, postoperative radiation treatment was applied up to 70.2 Gy to the primary site and 50 to 60 Gy to the cervical nodes. In all patients the clinical and histopathologic data were documented according to the guidelines of the DÖSAK (German-Austrian-Swiss Association for Head and Neck Tumours; Hausamen 1988). Only biopsy specimens of patients who had been enrolled in this study were investigated to ensure consistency of the data for statistical analysis. Because the biopsy specimens were small, not all investigations could be carried out for every patient.

In 10 patients who were diagnosed with leukoplakia or lichen planus of the oral mucosa who eventually developed carcinomas, 55 biopsies representing different stages of the disease had been taken over several years. Some of the patients developed recurrent malignancies. These tissue specimens were also enrolled in the study.

Fresh Frozen Tissue

From 1992 to 1993 biopsy samples of lichen planus, leukoplakia and OSCC were collected from 78 patients. In a large number of the OSCC patients multiple dental extractions of destroyed teeth were performed at the time of biopsy of the tumor. Therefore, it was often possible to collect clinically normal tissue from a distant site in the oral mucosa, if the patient consented. All biopsy specimens were immediately divided by a pathologist. One part of the tissue was fixed in 10% formalin, embedded in paraffin, and processed for diagnostic light microscopy as usual. Diagnostic histopathology was used to ensure that tumor cells predominated in the specimens. The other part of the biopsy tissues was snap frozen and stored in liquid nitrogen. Sections of frozen biopsy tissue samples measuring 5 to 10 μm were cut on a cryostat and stored at -20 °C until required for DNA analysis. Because the biopsy tissue specimens were small, not all investigations described could be carried out for every patient.

Blood samples

In most cases where fresh frozen tissue was collected, blood samples were drawn for further DNA analysis (eg, loss of heterozygosity studies). Serum was separated by centrifugation as usual and the samples were stored at −20 °C until required.

Cell Lines

Cell lines were grown in the appropriate medium as described below. For immunohistochemistry the cells were fixed in 10% formalin and then embedded in paraffin in chamber slides (Shandon, Frankfurt).

3.1.2. Histopathology

All tissue slides were reevaluated by one pathologist (G.K.) to ensure a consistent histopathologic classification. The epithlelial dysplasia grade in the benign lesions was classified histopathologically according to Gräßel-Pietrusky and Hornstein (1982) and Burkhardt (1985) (GI for mild, GII for moderate and GIII for severe dysplasia). The oral squamous cell carcinomas were classified according to the loss of differentiation (G1, G2, and G3 for well differentiated, moderately differentiated, and poorly differentiated OSCC).

3.2. Cell Culture

Cell lines of squamous cell carcinoma of the head and neck (HNSCC) and control cell lines with point mutations in p53 and Rb and impaired protein expression were grown in culture and used for immunohistochemistry after paraffin embedding as described above and for DNA analysis as described below.

3.2.1. Oropharyngeal Carcinoma Cell Lines SCC 4, SCC 9, SCC 15, SCC 25

Source:
ATCC (SCC 4: CRL 1624; SCC 9: CRL 1629; SCC 15: CRL 1623; SCC 25: CRL 1628)
References:
Cancer Res 41, 1637, 1981; Cell 22, 629, 1980; Cell 25, 627, 1981.
Culture Medium:
1:1 Dulbecco modified Eagles medium/ Hams F12, 10% FCS, 0.4 mg hydrocortisone/mL

3.2.2. Carcinoma Cell Line A-431 (Vulva)

Source:
ATCC (CRL 1555)
References:
J Natl Cancer Inst (Bethesda) 51, 1417, 1973.
Culture Medium:
Dulbecco modified Eagles medium/Hams F12, 4.5 g/L Glucose, 10% FCS

3.2.3. Glioblastoma Cell Line A-172

Source:
ATCC (CRL 1620)
References:
J Natl Cancer Inst (Bethesda) 51, 1417, 1973.

Culture Medium:
   Dulbecco modified Eagles medium/Hams
   F12, 4.5 g/L Glucose, 10% FCS

3.2.4. Breast Cancer Cell Line SK-BR-3

Source:
   ATCC (HTB 30)
Culture Medium:
   McCoys 5a medium, 10% FCS

3.2.5. Cell line Huh7

Source:
   Gift from Dr Willemann, DKFZ
Reference:
   Nakabyashi et al, Cancer Res 42, 3858,
   1982.
Culture Medium:
   Dulbecco modified Eagles medium, 3.7g/L
   Sodiumbicarbonate, 10% FCS,
   1% Penicillin/Streptomycin

3.2.6. Cell Line H209

Source:
   ATCC
Reference:
   Kaye et al, Proc Natl Acad Sci USA 87, 6922,
   1990.
Culture Medium:
   Dulbecco modified Eagles medium, 3.7g/L
   sodiumbicarbonate, 10% FCS,
   1% Penicillin/Streptomycin

3.3.   Immunohistochemistry

Immunohistochemistry was employed to detect tumor suppressor gene products, MDM2
and cell cycle specific proteins in paraffin-embedded tissue sections of benign and malignant lesions in the oral mucosa and paraffin-
embedded cell lines from oral squamous cell
carcinomas.

3.3.1.   Immunohistochemical Detection of p53

Different monoclonal antibodies which recog-
nize wild-type and mutant p53 were first tested
in tissue sections and cell lines with known
overexpression or lacking overexpression of
p53. Two antibodies (mAb PAb 1801, Oncogene Science; mAb Do 7, Dako) gave consistent and reproducible results and were used in
this study. PAb 1801 is a human-specific monoclonal antibody that recognizes an epitope near
the NH_2 terminus of both wild-type and mutant
p53 protein (Banks et al 1986).
Immunohistochemistry was performed in all
paraffin-embedded tissue sections using the
APAAP technique. Tissue sections were first
dewaxed with xylene (30 min) and rehydrated
gradually with ethanol and water. The tissue
sections were then incubated with 10 mmol citrate buffer (pH 6.0) in a microwave oven (750W)
for 10 min to resolve the protein fixation. TBS
treated sections were subsequently incubated
with rabbit serum (1:20, Dako X90210) for 10
min and then incubated with the specific antibody (mAb PAb 1801, Oncogene Science,
1:200; mAb Do 7, Dako 1:30) at 4 °C overnight.
After washing with TBS (10 min), sections were
blocked with rabbit serum (1:20, Dako
X90210) for 10 min followed by incubation with
the amboceptor (1:50, Dako Z259) for 45 min
at room temperature. After further washing with
TBS the sections were then incubated with rabbit serum (1:20, 10 min) and the APAAP complex (1:50, 45 min, Dako D 651). The steps starting with the rabbit serum, incubation with the
amboceptor, washing and incubation with rabbit serum and the APAAP complex were repeated once. After further washing with TBS,
the reaction product was stained with Fast Red
(Sigma F-1500) and counterstained with hematoxylin. Levamisole (1 mmol) was added to
block endogenous alkaline phosphatase activity. All incubations were carried out at room
temperature if not indicated otherwise. Each

set of experiments included SCC 4 as a positive control and normal mucosa as negative control. All stained nuclei were scored as positive regardless of staining intensity, because the loss of antigenicity of the protein may be due to tissue processing.

3.3.2. Immunohistochemical Detection of RB protein

Immunohistochemistry was performed using the APAAP technique. The tissue sections were first dewaxed with xylene (30 min), dehydrated with ethanol and rehydrated gradually with ethanol and water. The tissue sections were then incubated with TBS (pH 7.4) in a microwave oven (650W) twice for 5 min to resolve the protein fixation. The TBS-treated sections were subsequently incubated with goat serum (1:10, Dako X 907) for 10 min, followed by incubation with the specific antibody (mAb RB Ab-1, Paesel and Dorei 1:20). The RB mAb was incubated for 24 h at 4 °C. After two washings with TBS the sections were incubated with pig serum (1:20, Dako X 901) for 10 min, followed by incubation with the bridging antibody (Dako Z 259) for 60 min. The sections were washed again with TBS and incubated with goat serum (1:10, 10 min) and the APAAP complex (1:50, 60 min, Dako D 651). The steps starting with pig serum, incubation with the bridging antibody, washing and incubation with goat serum and the APAAP complex were repeated once. After a further washing with TBS, the reaction product was stained with Fast Red (Sigma F-1500) and counterstained with hematoxylin. Levamisole was added to a final concentration of 1 mmol to block endogenous alkaline phosphatase activity. All incubations were carried out at room temperature if not indicated otherwise. Each set of experiments included SCC 4 and H209 as positive and negative controls, respectively.

3.3.3. Immunohistochemical Detection of MDM2

Immunohistochemistry was performed on paraffin-embedded 3 μm tissue sections using the APAAP technique. Tissue sections were first dewaxed with xylene (30 min) and rehydrated gradually with ethanol and water. The sections were then incubated with 10 mmol citrate buffer (pH 6.0) in a microwave oven (750W) for 10 min to resolve the protein fixation. TBS-treated sections were subsequently incubated with rabbit serum (1:20, Dako X90210) for 10 min and then incubated with the MDM2 specific antibody (mAb IF-2, Oncogene Science, 1:75) at 4 °C overnight. After being washed with TBS (10 min), sections were blocked with rabbit serum (1:20, Dako X90210) for 10 min and incubated with the amboceptor (1:50, Dako Z259) for 45 min at room temperature. After a further washing with TBS, the sections were incubated with rabbit serum (1:20, 10 min) and the APAAP complex (1:50, 45 min, Dako D 651). The steps starting with the rabbit serum, incubation with the amboceptor, washing, and incubation with rabbit serum and the APAAP complex were repeated once. After another washing with TBS, the reaction product was stained with Fast Red (Sigma F-1500) and counterstained with hematoxylin. Levamisole (1 mmol) was added to block endogenous alkaline phosphatase activity. All incubations were carried out at room temperature if not indicated otherwise. Each set of experiments included positive and negative controls of human lung tissue (kindly provided by Dr Wiethege, Bochum).

3.3.4. Immunohistochemical Detection of PCNA/Cyclin

Immunohistochemistry for PCNA was performed using the APAAP technique. The tissue sections and embedded cells were first dewaxed with xylene (30 min), dehydrated with ethanol, and rehydrated gradually with ethanol and water. The cells and tissue sections were then incubated twice for 5 min with TBS (pH

7.4) in the microwave oven (650W) to resolve the protein fixation. The TBS-treated sections were incubated with goat serum (1:10, Dako X 907) for 10 min and incubation with the PCNA specific antibody (mAb PC 10, Dako, 1:100) for 12 h at 4 °C followed. After two TBS washings, the sections were incubated with pig serum (1:20, Dako X 901) for 10 min, then incubated with the bridging antibody (Dako Z 259) for 60 min. After a further washing with TBS, the sections were incubated with goat serum (1:10, 10 min) and the APAAP complex (1:50, 60 min, Dako D 651). The steps starting with the pig serum, incubation with the bridging antibody, washing and incubation with goat serum and the APAAP complex were repeated once. After another washing with TBS, the reaction product was stained with Fast Red (Sigma F-1500) and counterstained with hematoxylin. Levamisole (1 mmol) was added to block endogenous alkaline phosphatate activity. All incubations were carried out at room temperature if not indicated otherwise.

3.3.5. Immunohistochemical Detection of Ki-67

Immunohistochemistry for Ki-67 was also performed using the APAAP technique. The tissue sections and embedded cells were first dewaxed with xylene (30 min), dehydrated with ethanol, and rehydrated gradually with ethanol and water. The cells and tissue sections were then incubated twice for 5 min with TBS (pH 7.4) in the microwave oven (650W) to resolve the protein fixation. The TBS-treated sections were incubated with goat serum (1:10, Dako X 907) for 10 min and then incubated with the Ki-67 specific antibody (mAb MIB 1, Dianova) for 12 h at 4 °C followed. After two washings with TBS, the sections were incubated with pig serum (1:20, Dako X 901) for 10 min, followed by incubation with the bridging antibody (Dako Z 259) for 60 min. After another TBS washing, the sections were incubated with goat serum (1:10, 10 min) and the APAAP complex (1:50, 60 min, Dako D 651). The steps starting with the pig serum, incubation with the bridging an-

tibody, washing, and incubation with goat serum and the APAAP complex were repeated once. The reaction product was washed again with TBS, stained with Fast Red (Sigma F-1500) and counterstained with hematoxylin. Levamisole (1 mmol) was added to block endogenous alkaline phosphatate activity. All incubations were carried out at room temperature if not indicated otherwise.

3.4. RNA and DNA Preparation and Amplification by PCR

3.4.1. Preparation

Cell Lines

Cytoplasmic RNA was isolated from exponentially growing cells. After trypsinization, cells were collected by centrifugation at 2,500 rpm for 5 min at 4 °C. The cell pellet was resuspended in 10 mmol Tris-HCl (pH 8.0), 1 mmol EDTA, 100 mmol NaCl in DEPC-treated water and put on ice. $MgCl_2$ was added to a final concentration of 5 mmol followed by Nonidet P40 (final concentration 0.05%). After 10 to 20 seconds of vortexing, the nuclei were removed by centrifugation at 8,000 rpm for 2 min and immediately frozen at −20 °C.

The RNA solution was treated with EDTA (final concentration 2.5 mmol), SDS (final concentration 0.05%), 2 vol of Tris-saturated, prewarmed phenol (60 °C) and shaken carefully for 5 min. Phenol/chloroform extraction was repeated once. The RNA was precipitated with 2.5 vol of ethanol and stored at -20 °C until required.

For preparation of DNA, the nuclei pellet was resuspended in 2 mL PBS containing 200 μL proteinase K solution (5 mg/mL proteinase K in 20 mmol Tris-HCl, pH 7.5) and incubated at 37 °C for 1 h. After that 100 μL of STE buffer (0.5% SDS, 100 mmol Tris-HCl, 25 mmol EDTA, pH 7.5) were added and incubation continued for 1 h at 37 °C. Phenol/chloroform extraction of the DNA and dialysation in TE (pH 8.0) followed. The samples were stored at 4 °C until required.

Tissue Samples

Tissue samples were collected as described before. Some specimens had been fixed in 10% neutral formalin and embedded in paraffin. Other tissue specimens were snap frozen and stored in liquid nitrogen until needed. From each specimen 3 µm thick serial sections, and then 10 µm thick serial sections, were prepared. One 3 µm section was stained with hematoxylin-eosin for light microscopy. All slides were reviewed by one pathologist (G.K.) and graded as described in 3.1.2. For DNA analysis normal tissue was trimmed of as much as possible to avoid contamination with non-malignant cells (Hedrum et al 1994).

For DNA preparation, tissue sections of 10 µm each were incubated at 55 °C for 5 h in 25 µL of a lysis buffer (0.32 mol saccharose, 10 mmol Tris-HCl, pH 7.0, 5 mmol $MgCl_2$, 1% Triton x-100) and 2 µL of proteinase K (10 mg/mL). Proteinase K was inactivated by incubation at 95 °C for 10 min. The tissue debris was removed by centrifugation, and the DNA solution was stored at –20 °C until required.

Blood Samples

For the isolation of DNA from the blood samples 0.5 mL of a lysis buffer (0.32 mol saccharose, 10 mmol Tris-HCl, pH 7.0, 5 mmol $MgCl_2$, 1% Triton x-100) were mixed with 0.5 mL of the blood sample. After centrifugation at 10,000 xg for 1 min the pellet was resuspended in 1 mL of lysis buffer and centrifuged again. Centrifugation and resuspension were repeated three times. The pellet was then resuspended in 500 µL of 10x PCR buffer (10 mmol Tris-HCl, pH 7.5, 50 mmol KCl, 1.5 mmol $MgCl_2$, 0.01% gelantine, 0.45% Nonidet P-40, 0.45% Tween 20) and 6 µL proteinase K (10 mg/mL) and incubated at 55 °C for 5 h. Proteinase K was inactivated by incubation for 10 min at 95 °C. The sample was stored at -20 °C until required.

3.4.2. Amplification of DNA (p53) from Tissue Sections of Benign and Malignant Lesions in the Oral Mucosa by PCR

In the p53 gene, most point mutations are located in "hot spots" in exons 4 to 8. In this study the DNA was amplified by PCR as previously described (Saiki et al 1988). The target sequences of p53, exons 1, 4, 5, 6, 7, and 8 were amplified separately. Oligonucleotide primers were synthesized on a DNA synthesizer as follows:

Exon 1: 5' GTT GTG AAG GAG ATT AAA TAA GAT GG 3' and 5'GGA CTC ATC AAG TTC AGT CAG GAG 3'

Exon 4: 5'CTC TGA CTG CTC TTT TCA CCC ATC TA 3' and 5'CAT TGA AGT CTC ATG GAA GCC AGC C 3'

Exon 5: 5' CAC TTG TGC CCT GAC TTT CAA CTC TG 3'and 5' AGA CCT AAG AGC AAT CAG TGA GGA AT 3'

Exon 6: 5' GTT GCC CAG GGT CCC CAG GCC TCT GAT TCC TCA CT 3' and 5' GGA GGC CCT TAG CCT CGT AAG CTT CA 3'

Exon 7: 5' AAG GCG CAC TGG CCT CAT CTT GGG C 3' and 5' AGC AGG CCA GTG TGC AGG GTG GCA 3'

Exon 8: 5' GAC AGG TAG GAC CTG ATT TCC TTA CTG 3' and 5' GTG AAT CTG AGG CAT AAC TGC ACC CT 3'

A "hot start" PCR reaction was carried out with a 50 µL reaction volume containing 10 µL of the diluted DNA sample (1:10), 5 µL of 10x PCR buffer (100 mmol Tris-HCl, pH 8.4, 500 mmol KCl), 0.5 µL of each primer, and 200 to 400 µmol concentrations of each desoxynucleotide triphosphate (dGTP, dATP,dTTP,dCTP). 2.5 units of Taq polymerase (Gibco BRL) were added after the first denaturation step (95 °C, 5 min).

In general the reaction mixtures underwent

cyclical denaturation (93 °C, 50 seconds) followed by annealing (53 °C, 45 seconds) and extension (72 °C, 45 seconds) in a thermal cycler (Biometra, TRIO thermocycler). Routinely, 38 amplification cycles were performed, followed by incubation at 72 °C for 5 min and storage at 4 °C. Agarose gel (1 to 2%) electrophoresis was used to confirm amplification of the correct target sequences and the PCR-amplified DNA was purified (Magic PCR Prep, Promega).

3.4.3. Amplification of DNA (Rb) from Fresh Frozen Tissue Sections of Benign and Malignant Lesions in the Oral Mucosa by PCR

In the Retinoblastoma gene, most point mutations and small deletions are located in exons 13 to 23 and in the promoter region (Bookstein et al 1990; Horowitz et al 1989; Kaye et al 1990; Mori et al 1990; Onadim et al 1992; Sakai et al 1991). The DNA was amplified by PCR as previously described (Saiki et al 1988). The target sequences of Rb, promoter region, exon 14, exon 20, and exon 21 were amplified separately. Oligonucleotide primers were synthesized on a DNA synthesizer as follows:

Promotor: 5' GAT CCC AAA AGG CCA GCA AGT GTC T 3' and 5' TCA ACG TCC CCT GAG AAA AAC CGG A 3'(570 bp fragment)

Exon 14: 5' CTA AAA TAG CAG GCT CTT ATT TTT C 3' and 5' ATC TTG ATG CCT TGA CCT CCT GAT 3'(212 bp fragment)

Exon 20: 5' TTC TCT GGG GGA AAG AAA AGA GTG 3' and 5' AGT TAA CAA GTA AGT AGG GAG GAG A 3'(350 bp fragment)

Exon 21: 5' GAC TTT CAA ACT GAG CTC AGT ATG G 3'and 5' ACA AAT ACC TGC TTA TTA CAG GGA T 3' (518 bp fragment)

A "hot start" PCR reaction was carried out with a 50 µL reaction volume containing 3 to 5 µL of the DNA sample, 5 µL of 10x PCR buffer (200 mmol Tris-HCl, pH 8.4, 500 mmol KCl), 0.5 µL of each primer, and 200 to 400 µmol concentrations of each desoxynucleotide triphosphate (dGTP, dATP, dTTP, dCTP). 2.5 units of Taq polymerase (Gibco BRL) were added after the first denaturation step (95 °C, 5 min). The reaction mixtures underwent cyclical denaturation (94 °C, 30 seconds), annealing (58 to 62 °C, 30 seconds), and extension (72 °C, 40 seconds) in a thermal cycler (Biometra, TRIO thermocycler). Routinely, 50 amplification cycles were performed followed by incubation at 70 °C for 10 min. Agarose gel (1%) electrophoresis was used to confirm amplification of the correct target sequences.

3.5 Single Strand Conformation Polymorphism (SSCP)

3.5.1. p53 Gene

For SSCP 9.5 µL of the PCR reaction mix were withdrawn and mixed with 3.0 µL of 0.5 N NaOH and 10 mmol EDTA. This solution was mixed with 12.5 µL of a loading buffer (12.5 µL 95% deionized formamide, 0.25% bromophenol blue, 0.25% xylene cyanol), incubated at 95 °C for 10 min, and run a 15 to 20% polyacrylamide gel.

A sequencing type apparatus (Biotec-Fisher) with 20 x 40 cm glass plates and 0.4 mm spacers was used. Electrophoresis was performed in 0.5x Tris-boric acid EDTA (1x is 0.089 mol Tris-HCl, 0.089 mol Tris-borate pH 8.3, and 2 mmol EDTA) at 4 W for 24 h. DNA was visualized by UV-light after staining with ethidium bromide (0.5 ug/mL) for 5 min and destaining for 20 min.

Each gel contained PCR-amplified complementary DNA for each exon as a negative control to localize the bands of interest and DNA from cell lines or tumor samples with a known point mutation as a positive control. Consistent results from two or more gels and independent PCR amplifications were reported so that PCR artifacts could be ruled out. The SSCP analysis was completed before the sample numbers were decoded and correlated with the histopathologic diagnosis.

3.5.2. Retinoblastoma Gene

Prior to SSCP analysis the amplified fragments of exon 21 and promoter region were digested to reduce the fragment size using the restriction enzymes AseI (promoter) or SmaI (exon 21). Agarose gel (0.8%) electrophoresis was used to confirm the correct size of the digested fragments.

For SSCP analysis 10 µL purified PCR-amplified DNA mixture was added to 10 µL of dye mixture (95% deionized formamide, 5.5% glycerin, 0.25% bromophenol blue, 0.25% xylene cyanol). The samples were heated to 80 °C for 2 min and incubated on ice prior to loading. Electrophoresis was performed on a non-denaturing 17% (exon 14, 21) or 20% (exon 20, promoter) polyacrylamide gel with 0.5x Tris-boric acid EDTA (1x is 0.089 mol Tris-HCL, 0.089 mol boric acid, 2 mmol EDTA) without glycerol and electrophoresed at 20 to 30 mA for 16 h at room temperature. A sequencing-type apparatus (Biotech-Fisher) with 20 x 40cm glass plates and 0.4mm spacers was used.

After fixation with a mixture of 10% ethanol and 0.5% acetic acid for 10 min silver staining of the gels was initiated by equilibrating the gels in 0.1% $AgNO_3/H_2O$ for 20 min. The gels were then rinsed in H_2O twice and submersed in a reducing solution (15g/L NaOH, 100 mg/L $NaBH_4$, 1.2 mL/L formaldehyde/USP 37%) for 20 to 30 min followed by agitation in Na_2CO_3 (7.5g/L) for 5 to 10 min. Finally the gels were submerged in 2% glycerol/0.5% ETDA and dried at 80 °C for 1 h (gel drier: BioRad).

Each gel contained PCR-amplified DNA for each exon from normal tissue as a negative control to localize the bands of interest and DNA from cell lines or tumor samples with a known point mutation as a positive control. Consistent results from two or more gels and independent PCR amplifications were reported so that PCR artifacts could be ruled out. The SSCP analysis was completed before the sample numbers were decoded and correlated with the histopathological diagnosis.

3.6. DNA-Sequencing

PCR products (2 to 3 µg) were purified by electrophoresis on 1 to 2% agarose gels (Sea Plaque, FMC). Following electrophoresis the DNA band of interest was excised. Excess agarose was removed as much as possible. The gel slice containing the agarose was weighed, an equal volume of dH_2O was added and melted at 75 °C for 5 to 15 min.

The purified PCR products were used for direct PCR sequencing as described before (Khorana et al 1994). Dideoxynucleotide sequencing was performed with [32]p-dCTP (Amersham, specific activity 3000 Ci/mmol) and PCR amplification primers. The annealing reaction was prepared by combining 5 to 10 µL of melted gel containing template DNA with 1 µL of primer (15 pmol/µL) and dH_2O to 11 µL. The mixture was denatured by incubation at 100 °C for 3 min and annealing was performed by immediately placing the tube in ice for 5 min. 10 µL of the annealed DNA mixture was then combined with 2 µL of the 5x reaction buffer, 1 µL 0.1 mol DDT, 2 µL diluted labeling mix, 0.5 µL [32]p-dCTP and 2 µL diluted Sequenase, Version 2.0 (all reagents U.S. Biochemical) and incubated for 2 to 5 min at room temperature. 4 µL of this mixture was added to each of the four termination mixtures containing 2.5 µL of ddGTP, ddATP, ddTTP or ddCTP and transferred to 37 °C for 5 min. 4 µL of stop solution (95% formamide, 20 nmol ethylenediaminetetraacetic acid, 0.05% bromophenol blue, and 0.05% xylene cyanol) was added. The samples were electrophoresed on 8% polyacrylamide/8 mol urea gels. The gels were dried and exposed to autoradiography for 12 h to 4 days. Mutations detected were confirmed by sequencing the opposite strand.

3.7. Loss of Heterozygosity

3.7.1. p53 Gene

Allelic loss of the p53 gene was investigated using a sequence polymorphism within the 6th intron (17q13) of the human gene (McDaniel et al 1991; Chumakov and Jenkins 1991). With a 46% heterozygosity rate, half of the cases were expected to be informative. Up to 10 ng of genomic DNA was amplified from the tissue and blood samples in a 50 µL PCR reaction containing 10 mmol Tris-HCl (pH 8.3), 50 mmol KCl, 1.5 mmol $MgCl_2$, 0.01% gelatine, 400 µmol dNTPs, 20 pmol of each primer (5'GTT GCC AGG GTC CCC AGG CCT CTG ATT CCT CAC 3', 5' GGA GGC CCT TAG CCT CGT AAG CTT CA 3'), and 2.5 units Taq polymerase (Gibco BRL). The reaction mixtures underwent cyclical denaturation (94 °C, 70 seconds), annealing (65 °C, 40 seconds), and extension (72 °C, 20 seconds) in a thermal cycler (Biometra, TRIO thermocycler). Thirty-eight amplification cycles were performed, followed by incubation at 72 °C for 5 min. The amplified DNA was purified (Magic PCR Prep, Promega), digested with MspI (Gibco BRL) restriction nuclease, and subjected to electrophoresis through 1% agarose. DNA bands were made visible by staining with ethidium bromide.

In addition the TaqI polymorphism (17q13.1) was used for analysis as previously reported (Serra et al 1991). A point mutation (A to G) at codon 213 of the p53 gene abolishes a TaqI restriction site (CGA to CGG). The PCR procedure was the same as above using identical primers. After purification the amplified fragment was digested with TaqI (Gibco BRL) restriction nuclease and subjected to electrophoresis through 1% agarose. DNA bands were made visible by staining with ethidium bromide.

3.7.2. Retinoblastoma Gene

A variable number (n = 14 to 26) of oligonucleotide repeats CTTT(T) are present in the intron 20 of the Rb gene. Because of the presence of multiple alleles, the Rb1.20 DNA polymorphism is highly informative and can be used for the determination of allelic loss in tissue samples (Brandt et al 1992).

Genomic DNA was amplified from the tissue samples in a 50 µL PCR reaction containing 3 µL of the DNA sample, 5.0 µL of 10x PCR buffer as above, 0.75 µL 0.1 mol $MgCl_2$, 0.5 µL of 20 mmol dNTPs, 0.5 µL of each primer (20 pmol/µl) (5'AAG TAA GAA AAT CAA GCA CTT3', 5' AAT TAA CAA GGT GTG GTG GT3'). From the blood samples DNA was amplified in a 50 µL PCR reaction containing 25 µL of the DNA sample, 2.5 µL deionized formamide, 2.5 µL of 10x PCR buffer as above, 3.0 µL 0.1 mol $MgCl_2$, 1.0 µL of 20 mmol dNTPs, 1.0 µL (20 pmol) of each primer.

After the first denaturation step (95 °C, 5 min) 2.5 units Taq polymerase (Gibco BRL) were added to each sample. The reaction mixtures then underwent cyclical denaturation (95 °C, 50 seconds), annealing (54 °C, 20 seconds), and extension (72 °C, 20 seconds) in a thermal cycler (Biometra, TRIO thermocycler). Forty amplification cycles were performed, followed by incubation at 72 °C for 5 min and storage at 4 °C. Agarose gel (1.0%) electrophoresis was used to confirm the correct size of the amplified fragments.

For better separation of the alleles, 92 bp of nonrepeat DNA were cleaved of with Bst NI (New England Biolabs) by incubation of the 10 µL PCR mixture with 1 unit of enzyme at 60 °C for 6 h and 15 min at 95 °C. The DNA was purified (Magic PCR Prep, Promega) and stored at 4 °C. A mixture of 2 µL of the purified DNA solution and 3 µL loading buffer (0.25% bromophenol blue, 0.25% xylene cyanol, 15% Ficoll 400) was then loaded onto a 20% polyacrylamide gel. A sequencing-type apparatus (Biotec-Fisher) with 20 x 40cm glass plates and 0.4mm spacers was used. Electrophoresis was performed in 1x Tris-boric acid EDTA (1x is 0.089 mol Tris-HCl, 0.089 mol

Tris-borate pH 8.3, and 2 mmol EDTA) at 300 V for 20 h.

After fixation with a mixture of 10% ethanol and 0.5% acetic acid for 2x3 min, silver staining of the gels was initiated by equilibration of the gels in 0.1% $AgNO_3$/ddH_2O for 7 min (Sammons et al 1981). The gels were then rinsed in H_2O twice and submerged in a reducing solution (15g/L NaOH, 100 mg/L $NaBH_4$, 1.2 mL/L formaldehyde/USP 37%) for 20 to 30 min, followed by agitation in Na_2CO_3 (7.5g/L) for 10 min. Finally the gels were submerged in 2% glycerol and dried at 80 °C for 1 h (gel drier: BioRad).

3.8. Western Blot Analysis

Nuclear extracts were prepared from cell lines SCC 4, SCC 15, and H209 as described before (Schreiber et al 1989). Three hundred milligrams of protein were run on a 7.5% acrylamide stacking gel in a Tris-glycine buffer with 10% SDS at 40 mA overnight. Blotting was carried out in an electroblot chamber for 4 h at 0.5 A in a transfer buffer containing 192 mmol glycine, 25 mmol Tris-base, and 0.01% SDS. After blocking with 1x HBB, 5% dry milk and 1 mmol DTT for 1 h the nitrocellulose membrane was rinsed briefly in 1x TBS. Then 25 mL of RB mAb (245-mouse) or E2F mAb (SQ41-mouse) antibody were added and incubated overnight at 4 °C. After removal of the primary antibody a secondary antibody was added. After incubation for 2 h at room temperature, alkaline phosphatase development was performed with a developer containing 200 μL NBT (0.5 g nitrobluetetrazolium, 10 mL 70% dimethylformamide) and 100 μL BCIP (0.5 g bromochloroindolyl phosphate, 10 mL dimethylformamide) in 30 mL AP buffer (100 mmol NaCl, 5 mmol $MgCl_2$, 100 mmol Tris, pH 9.5).

3.9. ELISA Testing

A total of 61 blood specimens were collected from 39 patients with preneoplastic and neoplastic lesions of the oral mucosa. Specimens from 2 healthy volunteers were also included. The blood was allowed to clot. After centrifugation at 3000 rpm (Beckman centrifuge, G2) the serum was removed and the samples were stored at -20 °C. For the ELISA testing p53 96-well plates from Dianova (Hamburg) were used. The p53 protein is coupled to the bottom of the plates. The plates were washed five times with a washing buffer, 100 μL of a 1:100 dilution of serum was transferred to each well. For each patient two aliquots were diluted independently and investigated on the same mikrotiter plate. Positive controls (supplied by Dianova, Hamburg) were directly applied to the plate and subsequently received the same treatment as the other samples. After incubation at 37 °C in a wet chamber for 1 hour, the plates were again washed five times with the washing buffer. Application of 100 μL of the antibody-conjugate-solution followed. The plate was again incubated at 37 °C in a wet chamber for 30 min, followed by repeated washing of the plates with the washing buffer as described above. Following the washing step, 100 μL of TMB-solution were added to each well. The plate was incubated for 30 min at room temperature in a dark room. The reaction was stopped by adding 2N HCl. If p53 antibodies are present in the patient's serum, they bind to the p53 protein in the bottom of the wells. Then they are recognized by an antihuman IgG antibody coupled to peroxidase. After an artificial substrate for peroxidase is supplied, a change in color indicates the presence of autoantibodies. The absorbance is measured at 450 nm. Values significantly higher than the controls were considered positive.

3.10. Statistical Analysis of Data

The immunohistologic data were analyzed using statistical methods. Data were stored in an Excel 4.0 database and analysis was carried out with BMDP 7.0 Dynamic (programs 1D, 2D, 4F, 1L, and PLOT). Variables were described using suitable methods: continous variables in terms of their mean values with standard deviation, medians, and extreme values, discrete response variables with frequency tables.

For the preneoplastic lesions (leukoplakia and lichen planus) continuous variables (PCNA and Ki-67) were compared using the Mann-Whitney test. Values were considered significant below $P = .05$. No other confirmatory analysis was performed.

Statistical tests applied for the tumors included estimation of the median survival by the product-limit method (Kaplan-Meier) and calculation of the 95% Brookmeyer-Crowley confidence interval for the median survival time. The survivor functions were plotted. For comparison of the survivor functions across groups (localization, staging, grading, recurrence, monoclonal antibodies), the nonparametric linear rank test of Breslow was used; values were considered significant below $P = .05$. Only groups with sufficient numbers of patients were considered for comparison (Dixon 1992).

4. Results

Immunohistochemistry using highly specific monoclonal antibodies is a reliable and fast method for detection and localization of protein expression in tissue specimens, eg, expression of tumor suppressor genes such as p53 and Rb. The major advantage of this method is that it allows analysis of tissue sections with intact architecture. Thus changes in protein expression can be located in a particular cell or cellular compartment. Four different retrospective studies and one longitudinal study were performed with different combinations of monoclonal antibodies to compare the expression of the tumor suppressor genes p53 and Rb with the clinical and histopathologic data and the proliferation potential of oral premalignant and malignant lesions (Section 4.1.). As a result of improvements in molecular biology investigation techniques, it has also become possible to amplify single gene copies from small tissue specimens by polymerase chain reaction (PCR) and analyze them further, for example, by single-stranded conformation polymorphism (SSCP), DNA-sequencing, or detection of allelic loss (Sections 4.2. and 4.3.). Alterations of the tumor suppressor genes p53 and RB and their influence on protein expression can thus be studied in small tissue specimens and correlated with the histopathological and clinical data. These studies can elucidate the genetic changes that lead to malignant transformation of normal epithelial cells in oral carcinogenesis.

Mutations in the p53 tumor suppressor gene also give rise to the expression of conformationally changed p53 protein. Mutant p53 protein can be considered as foreign by the organism and may become the target of humoral response under certain circumstances. Anti-p53 response may therefore be a potential diagnostic or prognostic indicator in OSCC (Section 4.4.).

The data aquired in these studies was finally submitted to statistical analysis to evaluate the significance of tumor suppressor gene changes as biomarkers in oral carcinogenesis (Section 4.5.).

4.1. Detection of p53, MDM2 and RB Protein Expression and the Correlation with Proliferation Activity in Lichen Planus, Leukoplakia and Squamous Cell Carcinomas of the Oral Mucosa

4.1.1. Detection of p53 Expression and Ki-67 in Oral Carcinogenesis—a retrospective study

Eighty-five paraffin-embedded tissue sections of squamous cell carcinomas of the oral mucosa (OSCC) and 64 tissue sections of benign lesions (leukoplakia and lichen planus) were immunohistochemically stained with a monoclonal antibody for the presence of p53 (mAb Do 7, Dako), as described in chapter 3. The antibody recognizes an epitope between residues 35 and 45 of wild-type and mutant p53. To evaluate the proliferation status of the lesions, the tissue sections were also stained with Ki-67 (mAb MIB 1, Dianova). With the Ki-67 mAb cells in the G1-, S- and G2 phases of the cell cycle are recognized (Gerdes et al 1984; Key et al 1992). Therefore it has become possible to assess the proliferation activity in tissue specimens by immunohistochemistry. The Ki-67 mAb also binds to a cytoplasmic antigen in the basal cells of squamous epithelia (Rijzewijk et al 1989). Cell lines from SCC of the oropharnyx (SCC 4,9,15,25; ATCC) were grown in tissue culture as previously described. After fixation with formalin and paraffin embedding, the cell lines were also immunohistochemically stained for the presence of p53 (mAb Do 7, Dako). Of four OSCC cell lines (SCC 4,9,15,25), a detectable level of p53 was found only in SCC 4 (Fig. 5). Ki-67 was detected in all cell lines, as expected.

The benign lesions (n = 64) were classified according to the grade of dysplasia they showed. For the classification of dysplasia the nomenclature of Gräßel-Pietrusky and Hornstein (1982) and Burkhardt (1985) was used. Of these 64 tissue specimens (leukoplakia and lichen ruber mucosae), 39 (61%) did not show any dysplasia (G0), 22 (34%) showed a low-grade dysplasia (GI), and 2 (3%) showed moderate dysplasia (GII). One tissue sample was classified as severe dysplasia (GIII).

The squamous cell carcinomas (n = 85) were also classified according to the loss of differentiation the lesions showed. Forty specimens (47%) were well-differentiated. Two tumors were well to moderately differentiated. Another 40 tissue specimens (47%) were classified as moderately differentiated. Two tumors showed a moderate to poor differentiation. Only one tumor showed poor differentiation.

Expression of Ki-67 was found in all cases. In normal epithelium positive cells were found in the basal cell layer of the epithelium, whereas in dysplastic epithelium, expression of Ki-67 was also detectable in the suprabasal cell layers (Fig. 6). In the invasive tumors, Ki-67 positive cells were located in the periphery of tumor nests in highly differentiated tumors and randomly distributed on tumors with a low grade of differentiation (Fig. 7).

In the group of benign lesions without dysplasia (n = 39), 31 lesions (79%) did not show any p53 expression. A detectable level of p53 could only be found in 8 (21%) of the G0 specimens (Figs. 8, 12). In the lesions with dysplasia (G1 to 3) (n = 25) 9 specimens (36%) showed p53 expression at a detectable level (Figs. 10, 12). Notably the only G3 lesion was positive for p53, but only 1 of 2 G2 lesions showed p53 expression.

Forty-six (54%) of all OSCC showed a detectable level of p53 expression. In the G1 group (well-differentiated) (n = 40), 19 tumors (47%) were positive (Fig. 9). Among the OSCC that showed only moderate to poor differentiation (n = 45), 27 tumors (60%) were positive for p53 (Fig. 11). In 27 recurrent OSCC of the oral mucosa, 18 tissue specimens (66%) showed a detectable level of p53 by immunohistology (Fig. 12). The majority of the recurrent OSCC showed a moderate to poor level of differentiation (G1: n = 5; G2 to 3: n = 13).

The quantification of p53 expression in the positive tissue specimens did not show any correlation with histological parameters such as dysplasia and loss of differentiation. Similar to Ki-67-positive cells, p53-positive cells were commonly found in the basal cell layer and suprabasal cell layers in the benign lesions. In the tumors, focal or random distribution of the p53-positive cells was detected.

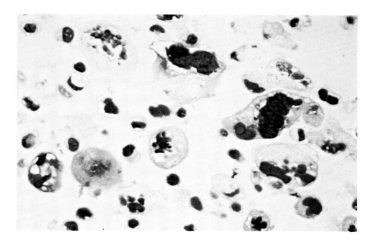

Figure 5: p53 Expression in OSCC Cell Line (SCC 4)

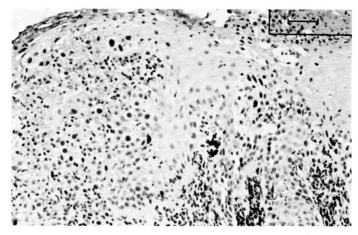

Figure 6: Ki-67 Expression in a Hyperplastic and Dysplastic Oral Lesion

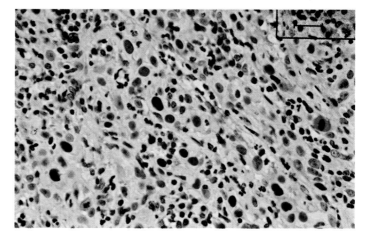

Figure 7: Ki-67 Expression in Poorly Differentiated OSCC

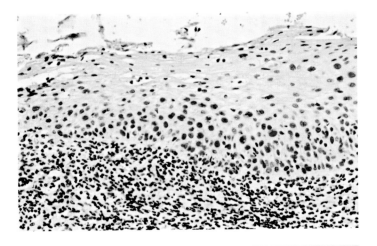

Figure 8: p53 Expression in Oral
Lichen Planus

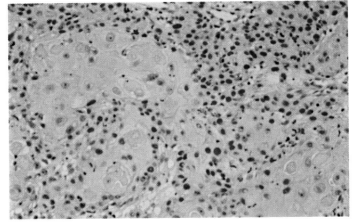

Figure 9: p53 Expression in a
Well-Differentiated OSCC

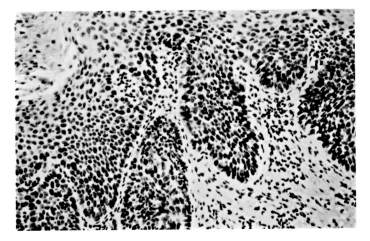

Figure 10: p53 Expression in a
Hyperplastic Oral Lesion

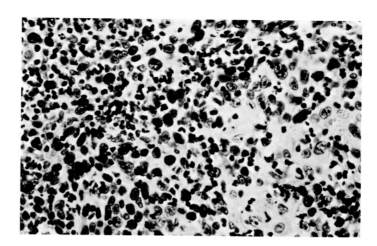

Figure 11: p53 Expression in a Poorly Differentiated OSCC

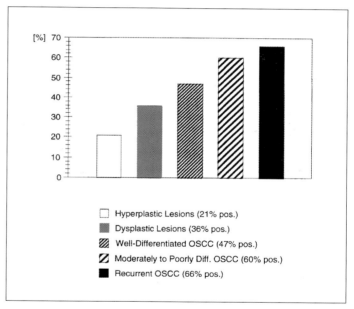

☐ Hyperplastic Lesions (21% pos.)

■ Dysplastic Lesions (36% pos.)

▨ Well-Differentiated OSCC (47% pos.)

▧ Moderately to Poorly Diff. OSCC (60% pos.)

■ Recurrent OSCC (66% pos.)

Figure 12: p53 Expression in Hyperplastic and Dysplastic Lesions, OSCC, and Recurrent OSCC of the Oral Mucosa

4.1.2. Detection of p53 and PCNA/Cyclin in Oral Carcinogenesis—a retrospective study

Paraffin-embedded tissue sections of preneoplastic lesions and normal mucosa of the oropharynx from 121 patients and sections of squamous cell carcinomas of the oropharyngeal mucosa from 144 patients were immunohistochemically stained with monoclonal antibodies for the presence of p53 (mAb Do 7, Dako) and PCNA (mAb PC 10, Dako) expression. Immunohistochemistry was performed as described. Proliferating cell nuclear antigen (PCNA) plays an important role in DNA replication and repair during the cell cycle. Because

49

PCNA can be detected by immunohistochemistry in paraffin-embedded tissues, it represents an excellent marker for the proliferation status of the investigated specimens (Kurki et al 1986, 1988; Morris and Matthews 1989; Scott et al 1991; Störkel et al 1993). PCNA reactivity to the PC10 mAb used in this study was expected in the nuclei of proliferating cells (Waseem and Lane 1990). Cell lines from SCC of the oropharynx (SCC 4,9,15,25; ATCC) were grown in tissue culture as previously described. After fixation with formalin and paraffin embedding, the cell lines were also immunohistochemically stained for the presence of PCNA and used as controls.

The preneoplastic lesions (n = 104) were classified histopathologically as described before. The squamous cell carcinomas (n = 144) were classified according to the loss of differentiation (G1, G2, and G3 for well-differentiated, moderately differentiated, and poorly differentiated OSCC, respectively). In the PCNA-positive tissue specimens, cell counts of the positive cells in 10 different areas of the slide, in defined size and standardized location, were performed to assess the PCNA expression semiquantitatively (Wintzer et al 1991).

Of 104 tissue specimens of benign lesions of the oropharyngeal mucosa (leukoplakia and lichen planus), 44 specimens did not show any dysplasia (G0), and 39 specimens showed epithelial dysplasia (GI to GIII). Twenty-one specimens were classified as lichen planus of the oral mucosa and in 17 the epithelium was normal. These specimens served as normal controls. The OSCC's of the oral mucosa (n = 144) were classified according to the loss of differentiation (G1 to G3). Of these, 67 were well-differentiated (G1), 64 were moderately differentiated (G2), and 7 tumors were poorly differentiated (G3).

None of the normal controls showed any p53 expression. In lichen planus 4 specimens (19%) showed p53 expression at a detectable level. In the group of hyperplastic lesions without dysplasia (n = 44), 16 lesions (36%) were p53 positive (Fig. 13). A detectable level of p53 was also found in 14 (36%) benign lesions that showed epithelial dysplasia. In the G1 group of the OSCC (well-differentiated) (n = 67), 29 tumors (43%) were p53 positive. Among the OSCC that showed only moderate differentiation (G2:n = 64), 32 tumors (50%) were positive for p53. Only 2 (29%) of the G3 specimens (n = 7) were p53 positive, whereas 4 (66%) tissue specimens from lymph node metastases of OSCC (n = 6) were p53 positive. The quantification of p53 expression in the positive tissue specimens again did not show any correlation with histologic parameters such as dysplasia and loss of differentiation. p53-positive cells were commonly found in the basal and suprabasal cell layers or were randomly distributed in the poorly differentiated tumors. In the well-differentiated tumors, p53-positive cells were often found in the invading margins of the tumor cell nests.

For semiquantitative analysis of PCNA/Cyclin expression, cell counts were made of the positive cells in 10 different areas of the slide, in defined size and standardized location. All specimens were PCNA positive. PCNA positive cells were usually located in the basal and suprabasal cell layers or randomly distributed in undifferentiated tumors, thus showing a pattern similar to p53 expression. In the normal controls an average of 27 cells were PCNA positive per field (Fig. 14). In lichen planus 56 cells were positive per field. In hyperplastic epithelium an average of 31 cells were positive, and in dysplastic lesions 47 cells per field showed PCNA expression (Figs. 15, 16). The number of PCNA positive cells increased in well-differentiated tumors (74 cells positive per field) and with loss of differentiation. In moderately differentiated OSCC (G2), 80 cells were positive per field (Fig. 17). In poorly differentiated OSCC and metastases of OSCC, the number of PCNA positive cells decreased again (60 cells positive in G3; 46 cells positive in metastases). PCNA was detected in all cell lines, as expected (Fig. 18).

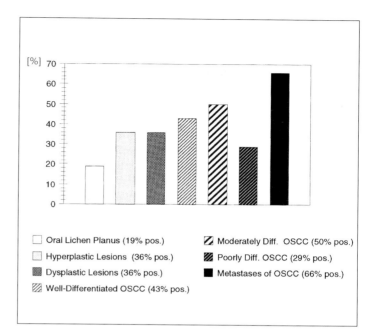

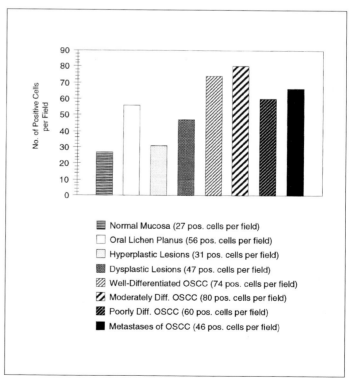

Figure 13: Positive p53 Expression in the Lesions in the Oral Mucosa

Figure 14: PCNA Expression in Different Stages of the Carcinogenesis in the Oral Mucosa

51

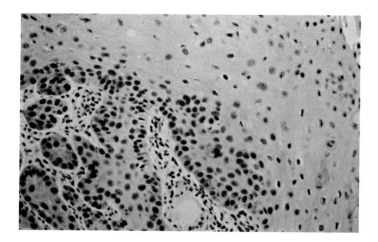

Figure 15: PCNA Expression in a
Hyperplastic Oral Lesion

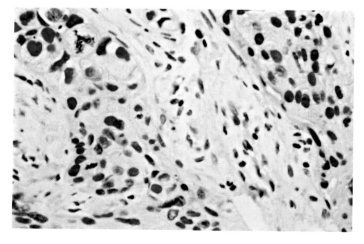

Figure 16: PCNA Expression in a
Dysplastic Oral Lesion

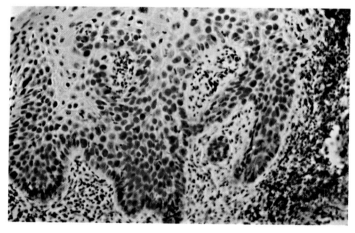

Figure 17: PCNA Expression in a
Moderately Differentiated OSCC

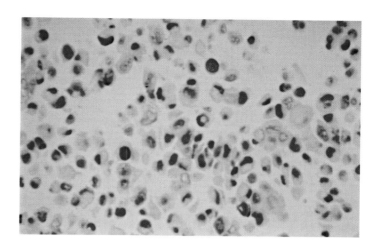

Figure 18: PCNA Expression in OSCC Cell Line (SCC 9)

4.1.3. Detection of p53 and MDM2 in Oral Carcinogenesis

Paraffin sections of preneoplastic lesions and normal mucosa of the oropharynx from 76 patients and from 110 patients with squamous cell carcinomas of the oropharyngeal mucosa were immunohistochemically stained with a monoclonal antibody for the presence of MDM2 (mAb IF-2, Oncogene Science) and p53 (mAb PAb 1801, Oncogene Science). PAb 1801 is a human-specific monoclonal antibody that recognizes an epitope near the N-terminal of both wild-type and mutant p53 protein (Banks et al 1986). The successful use of the IF-2 mAb (Oncogene Science) has been reported for immunohistochemical staining of the MDM2 protein in frozen sections of sarcomas (Leach et al 1993) and paraffin-embedded lung tissue (Wiethege et al 1994). We developed a method to detect MDM2 in paraffin-embedded tissue sections of biopsies of oropharyngeal mucosa.

All preneoplastic lesions (n = 76) and OSCCs (n = 110) were classified histopathologically according to the degree of dysplasia or differentiation. Tissue specimens were counted as positive for p53 or MDM2 expression when cells of presumably epithelial origin with positive nuclear staining could be detected. Cytoplas-

matic reactivities were not regarded as positive. Of 76 tissue specimens of normal mucosa and benign lesions of the oropharyngeal mucosa (leukoplakia and lichen planus), 51 did not show any dysplasia (G0). Of these, 14 specimens were classified as lichen planus of the oral mucosa and in 2 the epithelium was normal. In 25 tissue specimens epithelial dysplasia was evident. The squamous cell carcinomas of the oral mucosa (n = 110) were classified according to the degree of differentiation: 53 carcinomas were well-differentiated (G1), 48 were moderately differentiated (G2), 4 were poorly differentiated (G3), and 5 were lymph node metastases of OSCC.

In the normal epithelium neither p53 nor MDM2 was detectable. In the group of hyperplastic lesions without dysplasia (n = 51), 28 lesions (55%) were p53 positive and 16 (31%) were MDM2 positive. In 11 of those lesions (22%), p53 and MDM2 were expressed at a detectable level. In lichen planus, 9 specimens (64%) showed p53 expression at a detectable level. In 5 of those cases MDM2 was also detectable by immunohistochemistry. A detectable level of p53 was also found in 16 (64%) benign lesions that showed epithelial dysplasia. MDM2 was positive in 11 (44%) of the dysplastic lesions. Eight of these biopsies (32%) were MDM2 and p53 positive. Among the 110

OSCCs, 73 tumors (66%) were p53 positive and 51 (46%) were MDM2 positive. In 36 carcinomas (33%), p53 as well as MDM2 could be detected by immunohistochemistry. Overall the number of p53- and MDM2-positive tissue specimens increased during different stages in the oral carcinogenesis (Figs. 19, 20).

In oral leukoplakia specimens p53- and MDM2-positive cells showed the same localization and were commonly found in the basal and supra-basal cell layers. In OSCC specimens p53- as well as the MDM2-positive cells were randomly distributed in the tumors. Often p53- or MDM2-positive cells appeared in clusters, while epithelial cells in other parts of the same specimen did not show any reactivity. Semi-quantitative analysis of the number of p53- or MDM2-positive cells per tissue specimen was therefore omitted.

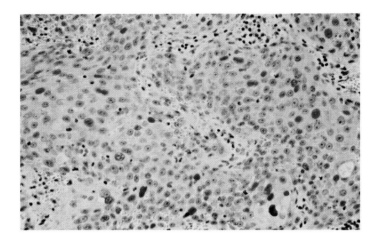

Figure 19: MDM2 Expression in a Moderately Differentiated OSCC

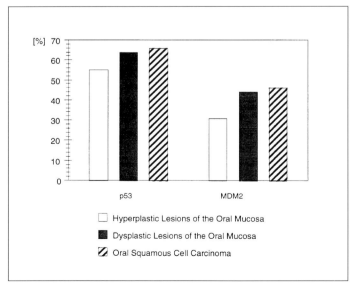

Figure 20: p53 and MDM2 Expression in Different Stages of the Carcinogenesis in the Oral Mucosa

4.1.4. Detection of p53, MDM2 and PCNA/Cyclin in Oral Carcinogenesis—a longitudinal study

Large areas of the oral mucosa often show premalignant changes of the epithelium and usually only relatively small biopsy specimens can be taken. Complete surgical removal of the leukoplakia is then not possible. The purpose of this study was therefore to investigate whether small biopsies are representative for larger areas of diseased mucosa, whether the status of PCNA, p53, or MDM2 expression changes in an individual case according to the stages of the disease, and at which stage of the disease p53 changes can be detected.

Paraffin-embedded tissue sections of 55 biopsy specimens from 10 patients who were diagnosed with leukoplakia or lichen planus and had developed carcinomas or secondary tumors were investigated. The biopsies were performed over several years and in different areas of the oral mucosa representing different stages of the disease. In one case biopsied tissue of the esophagus and the stomach were also available. The specimen were immunohistochemically stained with monoclonal antibodies for the presence of p53 (mAb Do 7, Dako; mAb PAb 1801, Oncogene Science), MDM2 (IF-2, Oncogene Science) and PCNA (PC10, Dako) expression as described. Because the biopsy specimens were small, in some cases immunohistology could not be performed for all monoclonal antibodies because of lack of tissue.

Positive p53 expression was detected with one or both antibodies in nine cases. In two cases all lesions were p53 positive in different areas of the oral cavity from the time these patients were first seen with oral leukoplakia until malignant transformation was detected 4 to 6 years later. Both patients have a history of heavy alcohol abuse.

One patient developed several primaries over 10 years (Fig. 21) (Table 2). This patient was first seen in 1982. A biopsy of the floor of the mouth was performed and revealed leukoplakia with mild dysplasia. In 1986 two biopsies in the left and right sides of the floor of the mouth were taken. Pathologic investigation showed carcinoma in situ. Both biopsies were p53 positive. The patient underwent surgery. Two biopsies taken in 1987 of the left side of the tongue and floor of the mouth showed only leukoplakia with severe dysplasia. The biopsies were p53-positive. In 1990 several biopsies of the anterior floor of the mouth were taken. The epithelial changes were consistent with carcinoma in situ. All biopsies showed detectable p53 expression. The patient underwent surgery again. In 1991 another carcinoma in situ was detected under the left side of the tongue that was p53 positive and was treated surgically. A p53 positive biopsy of the gingiva only showed epithelial dysplasia. In 1992 the patient developed a squamous cell carcinoma of the left side of the mouth floor. A surgical resection was performed. The tumor itself and a part of the resected epithelium that showed hyperplasia was again positive for p53 expression.

In four patients biopsies were taken in different areas of the oral mucosa, but p53 changes seemed to be confined to specific regions. In two of those cases p53 expression was only detected by the mAb PAb 1801 and only in the areas where carcinomas developed. One of these patients with erosive lichen planus developed several carcinomas, but showed p53 expression only in one area with hyperplastic changes. In four cases, including one of erosive lichen planus, the original lesions were p53 negative with both mAbs, but the malignant tumors that developed later were p53 positive with both antibodies. In one patient with concurrent tumors of the tongue, esophagus and the stomach, p53 expression was found in the esophageal and oral tissue, but not in the stomach.

MDM2-positive tissue was found in the original benign lesions in 5 patients independent of p53 expression and could not be detected later during carcinogenesis. In three cases, p53 and MDM2 expression were detected throughout the course of the disease. One patient showed only MDM2 expression in a benign hyperplastic lesion, but no further changes of p53 or MDM2 were found in the following biopsies. The proliferation capacity of all lesions was assessed semiquantitatively by counting the number of positive cells in 10 different areas of defined size and location in the biopsies. All hyperplastic lesions were p53 negative and showed an average PCNA score of 28 positive cells per field (Fig. 22). In the dysplastic lesions, the p53-negative lesions had a PCNA score of 50 and the p53-positive lesions had a score of 46 (PCNA positive cells per field). Among OSCCs the p53-negative lesions had a score of 53, and in the p53-positive lesions, 49 cells were PCNA positive per field. In general, the proliferation activity of dysplastic and neoplastic lesions was higher than in the hyperplastic lesions. The highest PCNA score was found in lichen planus. All lichen planus lesions were p53 negative, and 59 cells were PCNA positive per field.

Table 2

Patient	Biopsy	Local.	Histo.	p53 (Do 7)	p53 (1801)	MDM2
S.H.	6. 12. 82	FOM	Hyperpl./Dyspl. I	+	+	+
	6. 11. 86	FOM	CA in situ	+	+	+
	7. 10. 86	FOM	Hyperpl./Dyspl. II	+	+	NM
	8. 5. 87	Tongue	Dyspl. III	+	+	NM
	8. 5. 87	Gingiva	Dyspl. III	+	+	NM
	23. 8. 90	FOM	CA in situ	+	+	NM
	23. 8. 90	FOM	CA in situ	+	+	NM
	21. 5. 91	Gingiva	Dyspl. II – III	+	+	+
	21. 5. 91	FOM	CA in situ	+	NM	+
	23. 11. 92	FOM	OSCC G2	NM	+	–
	23. 11. 92	FOM	Hyperplasia	+	+	–

FOM = Floor of Mouth; NM: No Material Available

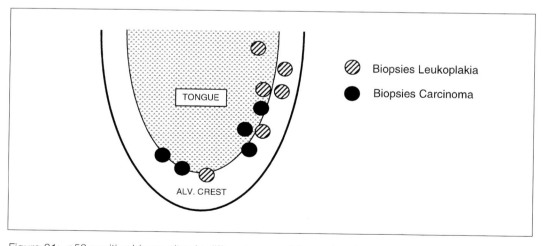

Figure 21: p53 positive biopsy sites in different areas of the oral cavity at different times during the carcinogenesis in one patient (first biopsy taken in 1982, last biopsy taken in 1992)

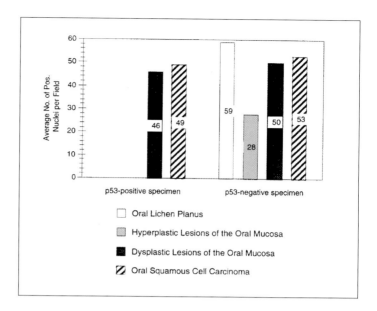

Figure 22: PCNA Expression in Oral Carcinogenesis

4.1.5. Detection of RB in Oral Carcinogenesis

Paraffin-embedded tissue sections of preneoplastic lesions such as leukoplakia and lichen planus, and OSCCs from 170 patients were immunohistochemically stained with monoclonal antibodies to detect the expression of RB (mAb RB Ab-1, Paesel and Dorei) as described. The RB mAb detects both unphosphorylated and phosphorylated forms of the RB protein. A method for the use of the RB antibody in paraffin-embedded tissue sections was successfully developed.

Of 70 tissue specimens of benign lesions of the oropharyngeal mucosa, 43 specimens did not show any dysplasia (G0). Twenty-seven specimens showed epithelial dysplasia. The OSCC of the oral mucosa (n = 105) were classified according to the loss of differentiation (G1 to G3). In 45 cases OSCC lesions were well-differentiated (G1), 53 were moderately differentiated (G2), and 7 tumors were poorly differentiated (G3).

RB protein is normally expressed in most tissues at a immunohistochemically detectable level (Cordon-Carlo and Richon 1994). It is not known though whether the presence of RB mutations correlates with a lack of immunostaining. In this study RB expression was detected in 89 of 105 OSCC specimens by immunohistochemistry and all benign lesions (Figs. 23, 24). A correlation with dysplasia grade or loss of differentiation could not be found. The RB-positive cells were located in the basal and suprabasal cell layers of the epithelium or randomly distributed in the tumors.

In the cell lines SCC 4 was p53 positive by immunohistochemistry. SCC 4 and 15 were RB positive by immunohistochemistry (Fig. 25), whereas the control cell line H209 with a mutation in exon 21 did not show any detectable RB by immunohistochemistry. Western analysis of several cell lines, including SCC 4 and SCC 15, revealed normal RB expression. In H209, where RB is mutated, only the hypophosphorylated form of RB could be detected, and immunohistochemistry was negative (Fig. 26). Thus immunohistochemistry seems to be correlated with expression of normal RB protein.

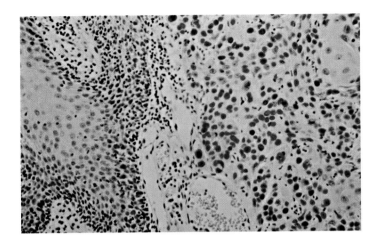

Figure 23: RB Expression in Hyperplastic and Dysplastic Oral Epithelium and OSCC

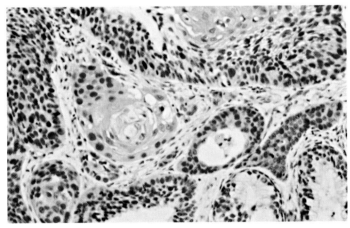

Figure 24: RB Expression in Moderately Differentiated OSCC

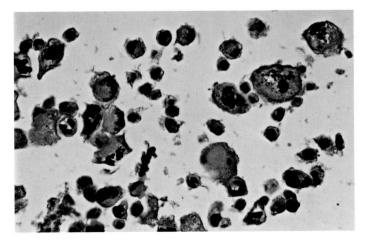

Figure 25: RB Expression in an OSCC Cell Line (SCC 4)

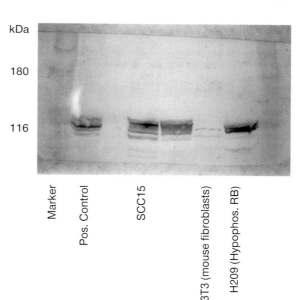

Figure 26:
RB Protein Expression in H209 and SCC 15

4.2. Loss of Heterozygosity of the p53 and Rb Tumor Suppressor Genes in Lichen Planus, Leukoplakia, and Squamous Cell Carcinomas of the Oral Mucosa

Loss of heterozygosity (LOH) at nearby genetic mapping markers can indicate the inactivation of known tumor suppressor genes. Amplification of DNA with polymerase chain reaction primers flanking the sites of DNA polymorphisms were used to compare DNA derived from matched sets of tumor and normal tissue or blood specimens of patients with oral squamous cell carcinomas or oral premalignant lesions.

4.2.1. LOH of p53

Allelic loss of the p53 gene was investigated using a sequence polymorphism within the 6th intron of the human gene (McDaniel et al 1991; Chumakov and Jenkins 1991). With a 46% heterozygosity rate, half of the cases were expected to be informative. In addition the TaqI polymorphism (17q13.1) was used for analysis as previously reported (Serra et al 1991). A point mutation (A to G) at codon 213 of the p53 gene abolishes the TaqI restriction site (CG to CGG).

Fresh frozen tissue and blood specimens from 40 patients were available for analysis. Mucosa specimens were collected from both the diseased areas and healthy ipsilateral or contralateral mucosa. All lesions were classified histopathologically as described above. Of 40 tissue specimens nine were benign oral lesions and included lichen planus (n = 4), leukoplakia without dysplasia (n = 4), and dysplastic leukoplakia (n = 1). OSCC (n = 31) were classified according to the loss of differentiation (G1 to G3). Eight carcinomas were well-differentiated (G1), 13 were moderately differentiated (G2), and 6 were poorly differentiated (G3). One case of a lymph node metastasis of OSCC and one carcinoma in situ were also included in the study.

Because alcohol and nicotine consumption are well-known etiologic factors in OSCC, all patients were asked about their habits. Twenty-three patients admitted to smoking between 5 and 80 cigarettes a day; 4 patients denied any smoking habit and for 13 patients data were not available. Eighteen patients admitted to drinking more than 1 glass of beer per day, and 7 patients were classified as heavy drinkers, consuming more than 10 glasses of beer daily and additional consumption of liquor.

In the normal tissues heterozygosity was observed in 26 (65%) of the 40 investigated cases with the MspI polymorphism. With the Taq polymorphism 18 patients out of 40 were heterozygous (45%) and thus informative. Loss of heterozygosity was observed in 7 cases using the MspI polymorphism (Fig. 27). In five of those cases loss of heterozygosity was also confirmed with the Taq polymorphism.

Advanced disease was seen in 6 out of 7 patients (Table 3). According to the TNM classification, the majority of the tumors were classified as T4 (3 patients) and T3 (2 patients), all with positive regional lymph node metastases (N1 to 2). In 1 patient with a T4 tumor the hyperplastic mucosa in the disease free resection margins showed allelic loss of the p53 gene.

Two patients had T2 tumors, one of them with fixed locoregional lymph node metastases. All tumors with p53 allelic loss were located in the floor of the mouth and the tongue. Six out of these 7 patients were moderate to heavy smokers and drinkers. In one patient no information about these habits could be acquired.

In 31 cases paraffin material of the same biopsies was available for immunohistochemistry. Expression of p53 was investigated, as described before, using two monoclonal antibodies (mAb Do 7, Dako; mAb PAb 1801, Oncogene Science). p53 protein expression was detected in none of the lichen planus lesions or the dysplastic leukoplakia. One hyperplastic lesion was p53 positive only with the Do 7 mAb. p53 positive cells were found in the carcinoma in situ, in 5 out of 10 well-differentiated OSCC specimens, and in 8 out of 13 moderately and 2 out of 6 poorly differentiated tumors. In 4 cases p53 expression was only detected with the Do 7 mAb, whereas in 1 case p53 expression was found using the mAb PAb 1801 only. In the 7 cases where LOH of p53 was discovered, three tissue specimens were p53 positive with both antibodies, and three specimens were p53 negative by immunohistochemistry (Table 3).

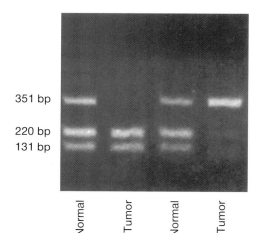

351 bp
220 bp
131 bp

Normal   Tumor   Normal   Tumor

Figure 27: Loss of Heterozygosity (Exon 6, MspI)

Table 3: LOH of p53

Case	Sex	Stage	Local.	Histo.	Do7	1801	Smoking	Drinking
B. W.	Male	T3N1M0	Tongue	SCC G3	neg.	neg.	++	+
E. M.	Female	T4N0M0	FOM	SCC G2	neg.	neg.	++	+
F. W.	Male	T4N2M0	FOM	SCC G3	neg.	neg.	ND	ND
H. H.	Male	T2N2M0	Tongue	SCC G2	–	–	+++	–
H. M.	Male	T4N2M0	FOM	SCC G2	pos.	pos.	+	++
M. R.	Female	T2N0M0	FOM	SCC G2	pos.	pos.	++	+++
P. T.	Female	T3N1M0	FOM	SCC G2	pos.	pos.	++	+++

FOM = Floor of the Mouth   ND = Not Done

4.2.2. LOH of the Rb Gene

Loss of heterozygosity of the RB gene was analyzed using a variable number (n = 14 to 26) of oligonucleotide repeat CTTT(T) in the intron 20 of the RB gene as described before (Brandt et al 1992). From 42 patients 75 fresh-frozen tissue specimens and blood specimens were available for analysis. Mucosa specimens were collected simultaneously from both the diseased areas and the clinically unaffected areas of the oral cavity. All lesions were classified histopathologically as described above. Of 75 tissue specimens 24 were benign oral lesions including lichen planus (n = 10) and dysplastic leukoplakia (n = 1). OSCCs (n = 47) were classified according to the loss of differentiation (G1 to G3). Fourteen lesions were well-differentiated (G1), 24 were moderately differentiated (G2), and 6 were poorly differentiated (G3). One case of a lymph node metastasis of OSCC and two biopsies of carcinoma in situ were also included in the study. In 4 cases the epithelium did not show any changes and was therefore classified as normal.

In the blood specimens heterozygosity was observed in 34 (81%) of the investigated cases. Analysis of 102 blood specimens of healthy donors also revealed a high heterozygosity rate (86%). Loss of heterozygosity was observed in 4 tissue specimens (Fig. 28) (Table 4). None of these tumor patients presented with very ad-

vanced local disease. One patient suffered from lichen planus. Only the lichen planus patient was a pipe smoker.

Forty tissue specimens, in some cases from different areas in the oral cavity of the same patient, were available for immunohistochemistry. Expression of RB was investigated as described before (mAb RB Ab-1, Paesel and Dorei). RB protein expression was detected in nearly all lesions investigated by immunohistopathology (n = 36). RB protein could not be detected in 3 OSCC cases (G1: n = 1; G2: n = 1; G3: n = 1) or the metastasis. In all cases where LOH of Rb was discovered, RB expression was detected by immunohistochemistry in the tissue specimens, indicating the presence of an intact protein (Table 4).

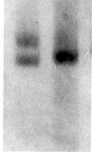

Figure 28: LOH of Rb

Blood   Tumor

Table 4: LOH of Rb

Case	Sex	Stage	Local.	Histo.	RB	Smoking
B. E.	Female	T2N0M0	FOM/Tongue	SCC G1	pos.	–
B. A .	Male	–	Lip	Lichen	pos	pipe
D. E.	Female	T2N1M0	Tongue	SCC G2	pos.	–
V. B.	Male	T1N0M0	FOM	Dys. GI	pos.	–

FOM = Floor of Mouth

4.3. Mutations of the p53 and Rb Tumor Suppressor Genes in Lichen Planus, Leukoplakia, and Squamous Cell Carcinomas of the Oral Mucosa

4.3.1. Mutations of the p53 and Rb Tumor Suppressor Genes in Oral Carcinogenesis - SSCP Analysis

Tumor Suppressor Gene p53

p53 mutations have been detected in many, but not all, human tumors. In tumors in which p53 mutation is not evident, several possibilities must be considered. First, p53 mutation could affect introns and is therefore not detected by most of the methods. Second, the function of p53 could be affected by interaction with other proteins in cell cycle regulation control. Third, p53 may not play a role in some tumors. Furthermore, p53 mutations are apparently not necessarily associated with detection of p53 expression by immunohistochemistry. High levels of p53 protein may exist without mutation of the gene being present, and deletions in the gene may lead to complete loss of expression (Rubio et al 1993; Rodrigues et al 1990).

To determine the correlation of detection of p53 expression by immunohistochemistry, proliferation activity (PCNA), and mutation of the gene, eighty-four biopsy specimens of 70 patients with benign and malignant lesions of the oropharynx were examined by immunohistology, PCR (Polymerase Chain Reaction), and SSCP (Single Strand Conformation Polymorphism). Immunohistochemistry was used as described in chapter 3 (mAbs Do 7, Dako; PC 10, Dako). Because most mutations in head and neck cancer are located in exons 5 to 8, DNA was amplified from paraffin-embedded specimens using the appropriate primers for these exons, also as described (Hollstein et al 1994; MacGeoch et al 1991).

All tissue specimens from preneoplastic lesions (n = 18) and squamous cell carcinomas (n = 66) were classified histopathologically according to the degree of dysplasia or differentiation. Among the benign lesions, 8 were hyperplastic, 5 showed epithelial dysplasia, and 5 were classified as oral lichen planus. The OSCCs showed varying degrees of differentiation: 35 were well-differentiated (G1), 28 were moderately differentiated (G2), and 3 were poorly differentiated (G3). The majority of the benign lesions were localized in the buccal mucosa (n = 15), followed by the floor of the mouth and the tongue (n = 2), and the hard palate (n = 1). Most OSCCs were located in the floor of the mouth or the tongue (n = 44), followed by the hard and soft palate (n = 8), the pharynx (n = 4), and the buccal mucosa (n = 4). Six tissue specimens were taken at other locations. Most tumor patients presented with advanced disease. At the time of first diagnosis 1 patient had stage I disease, 10 patients (19%) had stage II disease, 27 (50%) patients had stage III disease, and 16 (30%) patients had stage IV disease.

Immunohistochemistry indicated 39% of the benign lesions and 63% of the tumors were p53 positive. The proliferation activity (PCNA) increased with the dysplasia grade and the loss of differentiation in the lesions, but did not correlate with the location or the stage of the disease in the tumors (Fig. 29).

In the benign lesions the p53 expression and alterations of the gene as determined by SSCP correlated relatively well. Out of 7 biopsies in which p53 was detected, 5 showed mobility shifts in exons 6 (4 biopsies) and 7 (1 biopsy). Mobility shifts indicating mutation of the p53 gene were detected in hyperplastic and dysplastic lesions and in one case of lichen planus (Table 5).

In the tumor specimens p53 expression by immunohistochemistry and SSCP analysis were not well correlated. It has been postulated that the detection of p53 by immunohistochemistry is correlated with presence of mutation in the gene. Therefore, mobility shifts indicating mutation are not expected to be found in p53-negative biopsy specimen, but they are expected in p53-positive specimens. Among 27 p53 negative tumors, 12 (41%) mobility shifts were found in exons 5, 7, and 8. In 2 instances (17%) mobility shifts were detected in biopsy specimen in which only occasional cells were p53-positive. Only 12 (27%) of the p53-positive specimens showed mobility shifts by SSCP (Figs. 30, 31) (Table 6).

The mobility shifts detected were highly reproducible in the primary tumors (Table 6). In 7 patients 2 or more biopsies were made at different times or locations. Biopsy tissue taken from two different locations in the same tumor revealed identical shifts in 2 patients with OSCC (H.D. and P.A.), although p53 overexpression was not detected in the 4 specimens. Results from two biopsies of the same tumor before and after radiation treatment also showed identical shifts in the SSCP and overexpression of p53 (H.G.). In 4 cases (A.H., H.A., H.H., K.U.) the primary tumor as well as lymph node metastases in the neck dissection were evaluated. In all but 1 case (H.A.) the metastases showed the same p53 status with regard to overexpression and mobility shifts. In 1 patient (K.U.) the primary as well as the recurrent tumor and metas-

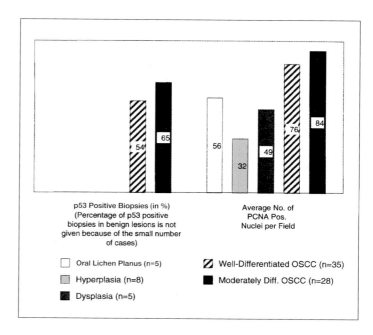

Figure 29: p53 and Proliferation Activity in Benign and Malignant Lesions

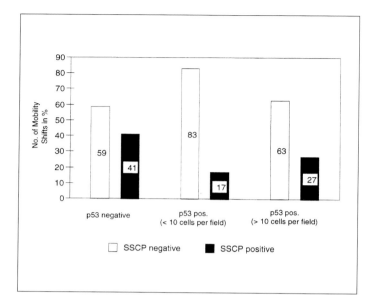

Figure 30: p53 Expression and SSCP Analysis in SCC of the Oropharynx

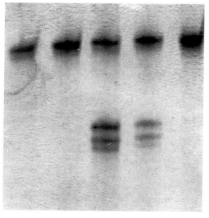

Figure 31: SSCP Analysis of OSCC (p53, Exon 8)

tases from this tumor showed the same p53 status in the immunohistochemistry and SSCP analysis. Alteration of p53, whether determined by immunohistochemistry or mutation analysis, was not correlated with survival of the patients.

Table 5: p53 Expression and SSCP Analysis in Benign Lesions of the Oropharynx

Pat.	Path. Diag.	Do7	Exon 5	Exon 6	Exon 7	Exon 8
B. L.	Dysplasia I	+	−	+	−	−
B. H.-J.	Hyperplasia	+	−	+	−	−
C. F.	Hyperplasia	+	−	+	−	−
D. H.	Lichen	+	−	+	−	−
L. C.	Hyperplasia	−	−	−	+	−
C. G.	Hyperplasia	+	−	−	+	−

Table 6: p53 Expression and SSCP Analysis in SCC of the Oropharynx

Patient	Biopsy	Local.	Do7	Exon 5	Exon 6	Exon 7	Exon 8
A. H.	9-89	1	neg.	+	−	−	−
	11-89	5	neg.	+	−	−	−
B. E.	3-90	1	pos.	−	−	+	+
B. K.	12-86	4	pos.	+	−	−	−
G. B.	6-88	1	pos.	+	−	−	−
G. C.	3-88	1	neg.	+	−	−	−
G. D.	6-90	1	neg .	+	−	−	−
H. A.	12-86	1	pos.	−	−	−	−
	1-87	5	neg.	+	−	−	−
H. D.	2-89	1	pos.	+	−	−	−
	2-89	4	neg.	+	−	−	−
H. G.	12-86	3	pos.	+	−	−	−
	1-87	3	pos.	+	−	−	−
H. H.	3-90	1	neg.	−	−	−	+
	4-90	5	neg.	−	−	−	+
H. I .	6-87	1	pos.	+	−	−	−
K. A.	10-88	1	pos.	+	−	−	−
K. G.	6-89	1	neg.	+	−	−	−
K. U.	3-92	4	pos.	+	−	−	−
	4-92	5	pos.	+	−	−	−
	1-90	4	pos.	+	−	−	−
P. A.	9-87	1	neg.	−	−	−	+
	10-89	1	neg.	−	−	−	+
V. J.	8-87	1	pos.	+	−	−	−

1 = Floor of the Mouth and Tongue; 2 = Buccal Mucosa; 3 = Maxilla and Palate; 4 = Pharynx; 5 = Neck

Retinoblastoma Gene

The retinoblastoma tumor suppressor gene encodes a nuclear phosphoprotein that is found in a mutated form in a wide range of human tumors (Bookstein et al 1990; Cheng et al 1990; Friend et al 1987; Fung et al 1987; Horowitz et al 1990; Hensel et al 1990; Lee et al 1987; Shew et al 1989). Rb plays an important role in the control of cell division and differentiation and seems to be ubiquitously expressed in normal human tissue, including squamous epithelium (Szekely et al 1992). It was the purpose of this study to correlate changes of RB protein expression as detected by immunohistochemistry with the presence of mutations in the tissue specimens.

In the Rb gene, most point mutations and small deletions are located in exons 13 to 23 and in the promoter region (Bookstein et al 1990; Horowitz et al 1989; Kaye et al 1990; Mori et al 1990; Onadim et al 1992; Sakai et al 1991). As the "pocket" of RB (C-terminal including exons 20 and 21) is sufficient for normal RB function in transactivation and binding assay, we focused on the analysis of exons 20 and 21. Mutations have also been described in exon 14 and the promoter. Therefore, these regions were also included in the analysis. Single-strand conformation polymorphism (SSCP) was used to screen for mutations in 42 biopsies of benign, premalignant, and malignant lesions and cell lines deriving from SCC of the oral cavity.

Analysis of cell lines from OSCC (SCC 4 and SCC 15) showed a good correlation between absence of RB mutation and positive staining by immunohistochemistry. The control cell line H209 with a mutation in exon 21 was RB negative and showed the appropriate shift in the SSCP analysis. No mobility shifts indicating RB changes were found in the tissue specimens, and all carcinomas investigated were RB positive by immunohistochemistry, indicating the presence of intact protein (Fig. 32).

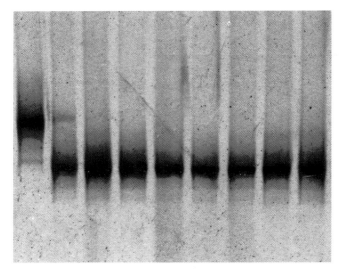

Positive Control (H209)

Biopsy specimens

Figure 32: SSCP Analysis of Rb in OSCC (Exon 21)

4.3.2. Mutations of the p53 Tumor Suppressor Gene in Benign and Malignant Oral Lesions—SSCP and DNA-Sequencing

From 5 patients 19 biopsy specimens of all disease stages were available that showed strong p53 expression. p53 immunoreactivity was detected with 1 of both p53 monoclonal antibodies in these cases (mAb Do 7, Dako; mAb PAb 1801, Oncogene Science). The lesions were classified histopathologically. Among the premalignancies, 1 lesion showed only epithelial hyperplasia, and in 9 lesions epithelial dysplasia was detected. Among the OSCCs, 2 were classified as carcinoma in situ and 7 as invasive squamous cell carcinoma. The speci-

mens were analyzed by SSCP and DNA-sequencing as described in chapter 3. Molecular analysis of the tissue specimens did not reveal any mutations in any of the lesions investigated either by SSCP or by DNA-sequencing in exons 5 to 8. In the SCC cell lines p53 expression was only detected in SCC 4. In this cell line a point mutation in the p53 gene at codon 151 (C to T) has been described (Brachman et al 1993). p53 expression cannot be detected in SCC 9, SCC 15, or SCC 25. In these cell lines deletions are present which probably impair the expression of intact protein. SCC 9 has a 32bp deletion at codons 274 to 285 (Fig. 33). SCC 15 also has a 32bp deletion at codons 274 to 283 (Fig. 34) and SCC 25 has a 2 bp deletion at codon 208.

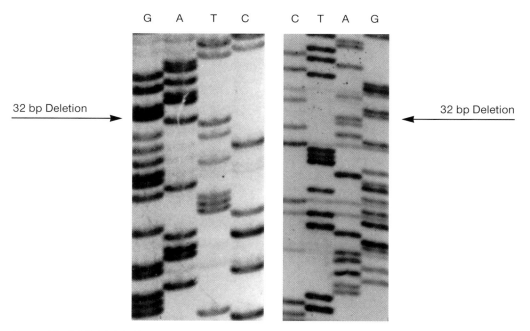

Figure 33: SCC 9 (p53, Exon 8)   Figure 34: SCC 15 (p53, Exon 8)

4.4. Detection of Anti-p53 Antibodies in Patients with Oral Squamous Cell Carcinomas

Mutations in the p53 tumor suppressor gene give rise to the expression of conformationally changed p53 mutant protein. Mutant p53 protein can be considered foreign by the organism and may become the target of humoral response under certain circumstances. It has been reported that about 12% of cancer patients contained anti-p53 antibodies in their serum, whereas no anti-p53 antibodies were detected in 164 healthy individuals (Crawford et al 1984). Anti-p53 antibodies have been found in different stages in colon, breast, lung and ovarian carcinomas (Labrecque et al 1993; Matlashewski et al 1986; Schlichtholz et al 1992). Anti-p53 response may therefore be a potential diagnostic or prognostic indicator also in OSCC.

A total of 61 blood specimens were collected from 39 patients' neoplastic lesions of the oral mucosa. For the ELISA testing of p53, 96-well plates from Dianova (Hamburg) were used as described in chapter 3. At the time of first diagnosis, the stage of the disease was deter-mined in each patient. According to the TNM classification, 4 patients had stage I disease, 6 patients had stage II disease, 8 patients had stage III disease, and 21 patients presented with stage IV disease. The majority of the tumors were located in the floor of the mouth and the tongue (n = 25). One or more tissue specimens were taken from each patient and classified histopathologically. In seven lesions the epithelium was hyperplastic. Four lesions were dysplastic. Among the OSCCs 6 were well-differentiated, 10 were moderately differentiated, and 3 were poorly differentiated. Immunohistochemical staining of the specimens with a p53 mAb (mAb Do 7, Dako) was carried out as described before. None of the hyperplastic lesions were p53 positive. p53 expression was detected in 3 of the dysplastic lesions, 6 of the G1 tumors, 10 of the G2 tumors, and 3 of the G3 tumors. Anti-p53 antibodies were detected in 7 of the 39 patients (18%) with oral cancer (Table 7). The majority of these patients presented with stage IV disease. In one patient with stage III disease (Z. K.) the original specimens were negative, but anti-p53 antibodies were detected in subsequent tests. In all but 1 case (S.A.) the tumors were also shown to be p53 positive by immunohistochemistry. In 1 patient (J.G.) anti-p53 antibodies could not be detect-

Table 7: Anti-p53 Antibodies in Oral Cancer

Pat.	Biopsy	Blood S.	Stage	Local.	Histo.	p53 (Do7)	Elisa
EH. J.	23. 6. 94	21. 7. 94	IV	2	SCC G3	+	pos.
EN. J.	22. 7. 94	11. 8. 94	IV	2	SCC G1	+	pos.
J. G.	9. 5. 94	14. 5. 94	IV	1	SCC G2	+	pos.
	18. 7. 94	28. 7. 94			Inflamm.		neg.
L. H.	5. 7 .94	14. 7. 94	IV	2	SCC G2	+	pos.
S. A.	4. 8. 94	4. 10. 94	IV	1	SCC G3	–	pos.
		10. 10. 94					pos.
S. F.	20. 7. 94	21. 7. 94	IV	2	SCC G3	+	pos.
Z. K.	20. 5. 94	8. 7. 94	III	3	SCC G1	+	neg.
		18. 8. 94					pos.
		18. 1. 95					pos.

1 = Maxilla and Palate; 2 = Floor of the Mouth and Tongue; 3 = Buccal Mucosa

ed after the original tumor was removed surgically. A biopsy taken at the same time (28. 7. 94) showed only inflammatory changes but no tumor.

4.5. Tumor Suppressor Genes and Proliferation Activity in Premalignant Lesions and OSCC - Statistical Analysis of Data

4.5.1. Malignant Transformation in Oral Lichen Planus and Oral Leukoplakia

In a retrospective study, malignant transformation of oral lichen planus and oral leukoplakia was investigated and correlated with immunohistochemical staining of p53 (mAb PAb 1801, Oncogene Science; mAb Do 7, Dako), MDM2 (mAb IF-2, Oncogene Science), RB (mAb RB Ab-1, Paesel and Dorei), and proliferation activity, (Ki-67: mAb MIB 1, Dianova; PCNA: mAb PC 10, Dako) as described before. The data of 113 patients who presented at the Department of Oral and Maxillofacial Surgery at the University of Cologne with benign lesions of the oral mucosa were analyzed statistically. Because the biopsy specimens were small, not all of them could be analyzed with all antibodies. Therefore, the number of specimens investigated may vary for each monoclonal antibody described.

The majority of the lesions were located in the buccal and vestibular mucosa (n = 60), followed by lesions involving the tongue and the floor of the mouth (n = 32). Fewer benign oral changes involved the lips (n = 8) and the hard and soft palate (n = 13).

The benign lesions were classified according to the grade of dysplasia they showed. For the classification of dysplasia the nomenclature of Gräßel-Pietrusky and Hornstein (1982) and Burkhardt (1985) was used (GI-GIII is mild, moderate and severe dysplasia). Of the 113 tissue specimens of benign lesions of the oral mucosa (leukoplakia and lichen ruber mucosae), 56 (49%) did not show any dysplasia, 23 (20%) showed low grade dysplasia (GI) and 9 (8%) showed moderate dysplasia (GII). Two tissue specimens were classified as severe dysplasia (GIII). Oral lichen planus was diagnosed in 23 (20%) lesions.

p53 expression using the mAbs PAb 1801 (n = 83) and Do 7 (n = 98) was correlated with the histopathologic diagnosis (Fig. 35). With the mAb Do 7, p53 expression correlated with increase in hyperplasia and dysplasia in the lesions, whereas the opposite was found for staining with the mAb PAb 1801. An especially large number of oral lichen planus lesions were p53 positive with the mAb PAb 1801. Expression of the MDM2 protein was investigated in 90 cases and was found more often in oral lichen planus than in other non-dysplastic oral lesions. The highest percentage of MDM2-positive specimens was detected in oral dysplastic lesions. The majority of the lesions, regardless of the histopathologic classification, revealed positive staining with the RB mAb, indicating the presence of an intact RB protein. Most p53-, MDM2- and RB-positive cells were located in the basal cell layer of the oral epithelium; fewer cells in the suprabasal cells layer stained positive. Thus, positive cells appeared to be confined to the proliferating cell layers of the oral epithelium. No significant difference was found when the location of the stained cells in nondysplastic was compared with that of the dysplastic lesions.

The number of p53- and MDM2-positive specimens was also correlated with the localization of the lesions in the oral cavity. p53 and MDM2 positivity was found in all areas of the oral cavity and the number of positive biopsies varied. With the p53 Do 7 antibody, which correlated well with the increase in dysplasia as defined by histopathology, the lowest number of p53-positive specimens was found in the soft and hard palate and the floor of the mouth, whereas with PAb 1801, p53 expression was highest in these areas.

The proliferation activity of the lesions was de-

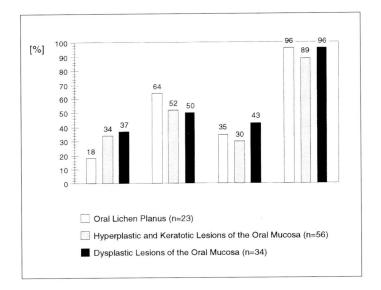

Figure 35: p53, MDM2, and RB
Positive Biopsy Results

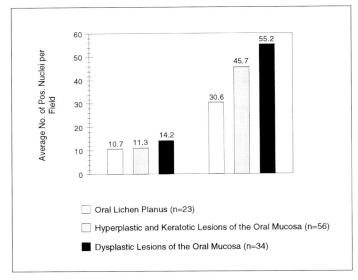

Figure 36: Histopathology and
Proliferation Activity of Oral Benign Lesions

termined semiquantitatively using the Ki-67
and PCNA antibodies as described before. The
highest proliferation activity was found in the lesions in the buccal mucosa (Ki-67: 13.6, range
= 0 to 53, median = 10.5; PCNA: 44.7, range =
6 to 94, median = 43.0), followed by the floor
of the mouth, the tongue (Ki-67: 9.4, range = 0
to 42, median = 7.5; PCNA: 39.5, range = 10
to 72, median = 33.5) and the lips (Ki-67: 10.2,
range = 0 to 27, median = 8.0; PCNA: 31.0,
range = 18 to 66 , median = 23.0). The lesions
in the palate showed the lowest proliferation
rate (Ki-67: 7.5, range = 0 to 28, median = 5.0;
PCNA: 35.9, range = 13 to 67, median = 33.5).

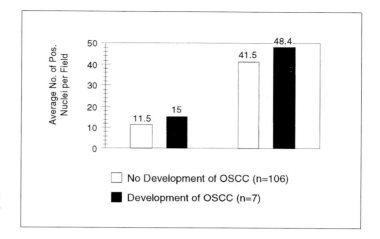

Figure 37: Proliferation Activity in the Originating Lesions and Malignant Transformation

Table 8: Tumor Suppressor Gene Expression and Malignant Transformation of Benign Lesions of the Oral Epithelium

Case No.	Sex	OSCC	Local	Histo.	Do7	1801	MDM2	RB
5	Male	1 month	Buccal	Dys. GI	pos.	pos.	neg.	pos.
30	Male	37 month	Palate	Dys. GII	neg.	pos.	neg.	pos.
86	Male	66 month	FOM/Tongue	Dys. GII	pos.	pos.	neg.	pos.
90	Female	119 month	FOM/Tongue	Dys. GII	–	pos.	pos.	–
91	Male	32 month	FOM/Tongue	Hyperpl.	pos.	–	neg.	pos.
106	Male	151 month	Buccal	Lichen	–	neg.	neg.	neg.
109	Male	29 month	Lips	Dys. GI	pos.	-	neg.	pos.

FOM = Floor of Mouth

In oral leukoplakia the average proliferation rate increased in dysplastic lesions (Ki-67: 11.3, range = 1 to 40, median = 7.5; PCNA: 45.7, range = 18 to 79, median = 45.0) in comparison with hyperplastic lesions (Ki-67: 10.7, range = 0 to 42, median = 9.0; PCNA: 30.6, range = 6 to 74, median = 29.0). The highest proliferation rate was found in oral lichen planus (Ki-67: 14.2, range = 0 to 53, median = 10.5; PCNA: 55.2, range = 13 to 94 , median = 57.0) (Fig. 36).
Seven patients (6.2%), 6 men and 1 woman, developed oral squamous cell carcinomas 1 to 151 months after the first biopsy was performed (Table 8). The patients who showed malignant transformation were slightly older than those who did not develop oral cancer (65.7 yr vs 57.6 yr). The majority of the OSCCs developed in the floor of the mouth and the tongue (n = 3), followed by the buccal mucosa (n = 2), the labial mucosa (n = 1), and the palate (n = 1). Most of the original lesions showed moderate (n = 3) or mild (n = 2) dysplasia. One OSCC originated from oral lichen planus and 1 lesion was hyperplastic. Most of the original lesions were p53 positive by immunohisto-

chemistry with either 1 or both mAbs. Only 1 lesion was MDM2 positive. RB expression was also found in the majority of the lesions, again indicating the presence of normal RB protein. The proliferation activity in the original lesions of the patients who developed OSCC was only slightly higher than that in the patients who did not show malignant transformation and was not statistically significant (Mann-Whitney test) (Fig. 37).

4.5.2. Tumor Suppressor Gene Expression, Proliferation and Prognosis of OSCC

Data of 103 patients were analyzed who presented at the Department of Oral and Maxillofacial Surgery at the University of Cologne with OSCC from 1986 until 1991. Biopsy specimens of the tumors of all patients were taken prior to therapy. The treatment regimen was standardized and consisted of locoregional radiotherapy (39.6 Gy) and simultaneous infusion of Cisplatinum on days 1 to 5 (20 mg/m^2 body surface), followed by radical en-bloc surgery of the primary tumor and the cervical lymph nodes. If the tumor margins were positive after surgery and in cases with extracapsular lymph node extension, postoperative radiation treatment was applied up to 70.2 Gy to the primary site and 50 to 60 Gy to the cervical nodes. In all patients the clinical and histopathologic data was documented according to the guidelines of the DÖSAK. Only biopsy specimens of patients who had been enrolled in this study were investigated to ensure consistency of the data for statistical analysis. Because the biopsy specimens were small, not all investigations could be carried out in every patient. The number of specimens investigated may therefore vary in each monoclonal antibody described.

In a retrospective immunohistochemical study, comparison was made between the presence or absence of p53 (mAb PAb 1801, Oncogene Science; mAb Do 7, Dako), MDM2 (mAb IF-2, Oncogene Science), RB (mAb RB Ab-1, Paesel and Dorei), as well as proliferation activity

(Ki-67: mAb MIB 1, Dianova; PCNA: mAb PC 10, Dako) in oral squamous cell carcinoma and the following: clinical staging, location, histologic differentiation grade, and survival.

The average age of the 79 men and 24 women was 57.1 years (range = 35 to 82, median = 58). The median survival time was 54.4 months (range = 3 to 96). The follow-up time of all patients was 37.6 months (range = 3 to 96, median = 96). During this time 37 patients developed locoregional recurrences, which showed a significant negative correlation with survival (P<.01; Breslow test). In addition, 60 patients (58%) died and 4 patients were lost to follow-up.

The majority of the tumors were located in the floor of the mouth and the tongue (n = 53), followed by the buccal and vestibular mucosa (n = 38). Few tumors involved the hard and soft palate (n = 12). Location of the tumors did not have a significant effect on the survival rate.

The tumors were classified histopathologically according to the differentiation grade. Of the 103 tissue specimens 51 (50%) were well-differentiated, 49 (48%) were moderately differentiated, and only 3 were poorly differentiated. Tumor grading did not have a significant effect on the survival rate.

At the time of first diagnosis the stage of the disease was determined in each patient. According to the TNM classification, 2 patients had stage I disease, 24 had stage II disease, 46 had stage III disease, and 31 presented with stage IV disease. Tumor stage did not have a significant effect on the survival rate, although the proliferation rate of the tumors seemed to increase with more advanced stages of the disease (mAb PCNA; Stage I: 50.5, range = 49.0 to 52.0, median = 50.5; Stage II: 65.8, range = 36.0 to 121.0, median = 64.0; Stage III: 84.1, range = 25.0 to 175.0, median = 84.0; Stage IV: 81.7, range = 36.0 to 146.0, median = 76.0). p53 expression using the mAbs PAb 1801 (n = 86) and Do 7 (n = 102) was correlated with the histopathologic diagnosis (Fig. 38). The number of p53 positive specimens increased further in comparison with the preneoplastic lesion, although no significant correlation with the tumor grading could be established. Ex-

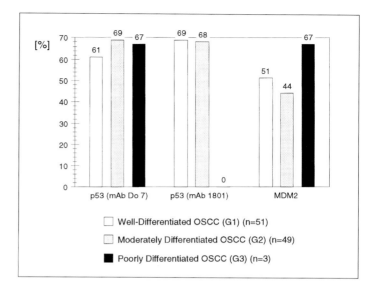

Figure 38: Tumor Grading and p53 or MDM2 Positive Biopsies

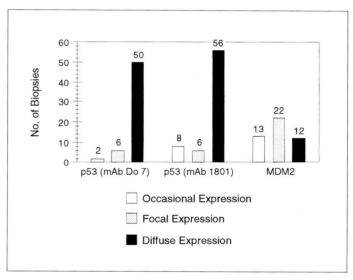

Figure 39: Expression Pattern of p53 and MDM2 in OSCC

pression of the MDM2 protein was investigated in 98 cases. Again MDM2 expression was found more often in OSCC than in preneoplastic oral lesions. The majority of the lesions, regardless of the histopathologic classification, revealed positive staining with the RB mAb (86% positive), indicating the presence of an intact RB protein in most OSCCs.

Distribution of the positively stained cells was investigated for all four antibodies (Fig. 39). In general, more cells stained positive with the Do 7 mAb than with the PAb 1801 mAb or the MDM2 mAb. With the p53 mAbs in a few cases positive cells were only found occasionally in the specimens. Usually, a higher number of cells stained positive and the cells showed a

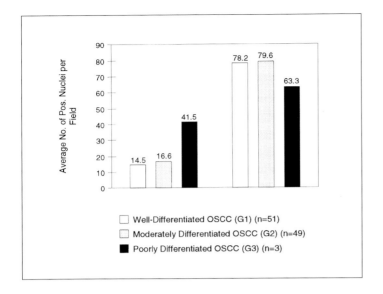

Figure 40: Tumor Grading and Proliferation Activity of OSCC

focal or diffuse distribution pattern. A focal distribution pattern was detected in fewer specimens than the diffuse pattern and seemed more likely to be found in well-differentiated OSCC, where the less differentiated cells at the margins of the tumor cell nest stained positive. In moderately or poorly differentiated tumors the positive cells were distributed randomly. With the MDM2 mAb, a focal expression pattern was found most often, followed by occasional and random expression.

In OSCC the average proliferation rate increased with loss of differentiation from well (G1: Ki-67: 14.5, range = 1 to 82.2, median = 8.4; PCNA: 78.2, range = 25.0 to 175.0, median = 74.0) to moderately differentiated tumors (G2: Ki-67: 16.6, range = 1 to 85.3, median = 13.0; PCNA: 79.6, range = 37.0 to 134.0, median = 79.0). There were only three poorly differentiated tumors available for investigation and the data may therefore not be representative. Ki-67 showed a further increasing proliferation rate, whereas the PCNA score decreased (G3: Ki-67: 41.6, range = 6.3 to 109.6, median = 8.8; PCNA: 63.3, range = 49.0 to 78.0, median = 63.0) (Fig. 40).

The proliferation activity and p53, as well as MDM2 and RB expression, were correlated with survival rate to determine whether they could be used as prognostic markers. Neither detection of p53 or MDM2 nor RB in the tumors showed a significant correlation.

Based on the available data, the average proliferation rate was calculated for Ki-67 (upper quartile = 19.6 => limit = 20) and PCNA (upper quartile = 95 => limit = 95). Patients with tumors showing an above average proliferation rate (>20 cells per field; 95% confidence interval = 10.0; 50.0) as determined by Ki-67 showed a significantly worse prognosis though in comparison with patients whose tumors showed below average proliferation (<20 cells per field; 95% confidence interval = 39.0; 80.0) ($P<.05$; Breslow test) (Fig. 41).

Surprisingly, just the opposite was found when the mAb PCNA was used. Patients with tumors showing an above average proliferation rate (>95 cells per field; 95% confidence interval = 28.0; 84.0) seemed to show a better prognosis in comparison with patients whose tumors showed below average proliferation (<95 cells per field; 95% confidence interval = 25.0; 56.0). However, the difference was not statistically significant (Breslow test) (Fig. 42).

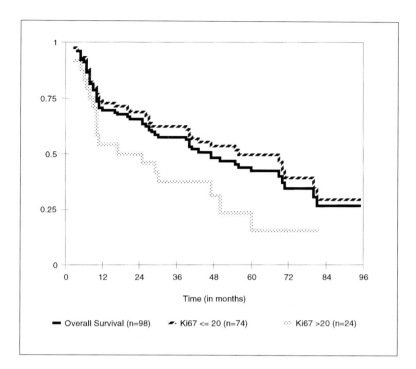

Figure 41: Proliferation (Ki-67) and Survival in OSCC

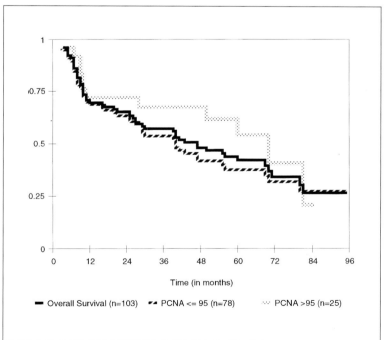

Figure 42: Proliferation (PCNA) and Survival in OSCC

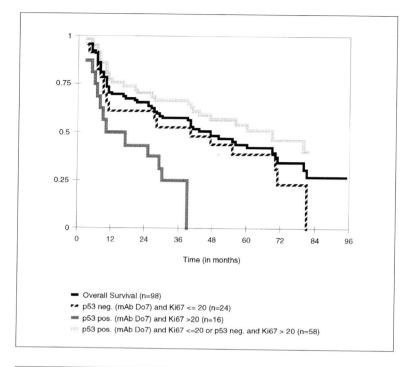

Figure 43: p53 Expression, Proliferation (Ki-67) and Survival in OSCC

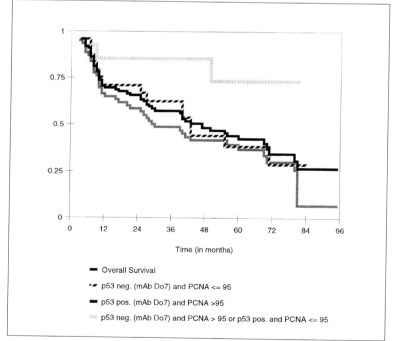

Figure 44: p53 Expression, Proliferation (PCNA) and Survival in OSCC

When p53 expression (mAb Do 7) and proliferation activity (Ki-67) were investigated for their relation with the OSCC survival rates, the combination of a below average proliferation rate (Ki-67 <20 cells per field) and p53 negativity were prognostically significant for more favorable course of the disease (median = survival time 34.6 months; range = 10.0 to 71.0). Patients with a high proliferation rate (Ki-67 >20 cells per field) and positive p53 expression showed a less favorable outcome (median = survival time 10.0 months; range = 7.0 to 30.0) (P<.01, Breslow test) (Fig. 43). In addition, patients with p53 positivity combined with a below average proliferation rate (Ki-67 <20 cells per field) or p53 negativity with an above average proliferation rate (Ki-67 >20 cells per field) showed a less favorable outcome in comparison with the overall survival in the group.
p53 expression (mAb Do 7) and proliferation activity (PCNA) were also investigated concerning the survival in OSCC. Again the combination of a below average proliferation rate (<95 cells per field) and p53 negativity appeared to be correlated with a less favorable course of the disease (median = survival time 45.3 month; min. 25.0/max. 82.0). Patients with a high proliferation rate (>95 cells per field) and positive p53 expression showed a more favorable outcome, though statistical significance could not be established (P=.07, Breslow test) (Fig. 44). The median = survival time could not be calculated in the later group because of the low number of dying patients. The survival of patients with p53 positivity combined with a below average proliferation rate (PCNA <95 cells per field) or p53 negativity with an above average proliferation rate (PCNA >95 cells per field) was not significantly different from the overall survival in the group.

5. Discussion

5.1. Genetic Changes and Inactivation of Tumor Suppressor Genes in Multistep Oral Carcinogenesis

Carcinomas constitute the largest category of human cancer, and they are the most complicated from a genetic point of view. In cancer of the upper aerodigestive tract, including oral cancers, there are no pedigrees demonstrating segregation of a dominant inherited predisposition. This is possibly due to the fact that alcohol and nicotine abuse cause the largest number of tumors in this area.

Oral carcinogenesis is believed to be a series of events that starts with the initiation of the oral epithelium. In this first step stable DNA changes are induced by carcinogens. An initiated clone of cells then expands, resulting in premalignant changes such as oral leukoplakia, a step that is known as promotion. Finally, some clones acquire the ability to invade the surrounding tissue, resulting in oral squamous cell carcinoma (Farber 1984). Analysis of colon cancer has shown that genetic changes accumulate during multistep tumor development (Fearon and Vogelstein 1990). The genetic alterations involved in the malignant transformation of a special cell or tissue type seem to be fairly typical, though the pathways are different in tumors of different origin. Apparently, genetic changes do not have to occur in a defined order. The accumulation of those changes seems to be of greater importance.

In premalignant and malignant oral lesions, increasing aneuploidy has been found and correlated with histopathology and clinical outcome, indicating accumulation of genetic alteration during oral carcinogenesis (Böcking et al 1985; Borg et al 1992; Burgio et al 1992; Hemmer et al 1990; Kahn et al 1992; Kokal et al 1988; Nylander et al 1994; Suzuki et al 1994; Tytor et al 1990). Chromosomal changes found in cytogenetic and in situ hybridization studies provide evidence that specific events are required in malignant transformation in the oral epithelium and seem to occur early in the carcinogenesis (Cowan et al 1992; Jin and Mertens 1993; Owens et al 1992). Voravud et al (1993) found no chromosome polysomy in normal oral epithelium from cancer-free individuals, whereas histologically normal epithelium adjacent to the tumors showed squamous cells with polysomies for chromosomes 7 and 17. The frequency of cells with polysomy increased as the tissues passed from histologically normal epithelium to hyperplasia to dysplasia to cancer. Recent investigations in oral leukoplakia showed that more than half of dysplastic lesions already harbor genetic alterations and progress into oral squamous cell carcinoma (OSCC), whereas only one out of six patients with hyperplasia show evidence of chromosomal polysomy (Lee et al 1993b).

Analysis of cancer cell lines deriving from primary tumors of oropharyngeal epithelium revealed gross cytogenetic abnormalities such as deletions, amplifications and translocations. They include breakpoints at sites 1p36, 1p22, 9q32, 11q13, 11q23, and loss of chromosomes 13q12-q24 (retinoblastoma gene) and 17p (p53 gene) (Carey et al 1993a, 1993b; Owens et al 1992). The cell clones were closely related, suggesting a monoclonal origin of the tumors (Carey et al 1989, 1993a, 1993b; van Dyke et al 1993).

Amplification of certain genes has also been studied in head and neck squamous cell carcinoma (HNSCC) using known markers (Nawroz et al 1994). Amplification of chromosome 11q13 seems to be an especially prominent event in HNSCC and is correlated with an aggressive histologic appearance (Lammie et al 1991; Muller et al 1994; Williams et al 1993). PRAD-1/cyclin D1 gene amplification is associated with advanced stages in head and neck cancer and overexpression may be of prognostic significance also for OSCC (Callender et al 1994, Jares et al 1994). Cyclin D1/PRAD1 was assumed to be an important target of 11q13 amplifications in HNSCC, but rare cases with more limited amplicon size suggest that one or more other relevant genes may be involved (Williams et al 1993). Loss of chromosome 9p21-22 is also reported in head and neck cancer progression (Cairns et al 1994; Sen 1993; van der Riet et al 1994). Furthermore, alteration of 3p seems to be a frequent event in HNSCC (Maestro et al 1993; Partridge et al 1994). The detection of nonrandom genetic changes in malignant transformation of the oropharyngeal epithelium supports the concept of field cancerization due to common carcinogens.

5.1.1. p53 Alterations in Oral Carcinogenesis

The series of genetic changes that leads to the development of squamous cell carcinomas of the oropharyngeal mucosa also includes oncogenes and tumor suppressor genes that may be markers of different stages of oral carcinogenesis (Carey et al 1993a, 1993b; Eversole and Sapp 1993; Field 1992; Issing et al 1993; Saranath et al 1993; Scully 1992a, 1992b, 1993). Loss of function of the p53 tumor suppressor gene is involved in nearly all human cancers (Hollstein et al 1991, 1994a, 1994b). Cells with inactivation of p53 have a growth advantage over their neighbors and do not respond adequately to DNA-damaging agents.

Thus, inactivation of the p53 tumor suppressor gene is probably an important event in oral carcinogenesis and may even lead to acquisition of other mutations.

The most common mechanism of loss of p53 function is through point mutation of the gene, resulting in the expression of a conformationally altered protein (Cho et al 1994; Clore et al 1994). Recent studies have shown that p53 mutation is a common genetic change in human oral cancer. Most cell lines of SCC of the oropharynx show mutations of the p53 tumor suppressor gene (Burns et al 1993; Caamano 1993; Chang et al 1992; Gusterson et al 1991; Jung et al 1992; Sakai and Tsuchida 1992; Somers et al 1992; Yin et al 1993) (Figs. 33, 34) (Table 9). Because cultured cells may be subject to in vitro selection pressure they may not be representative for the in vivo situation. Carey (1985), however, reported that cell lines of SCC inoculated in nude mice produce the same histologic features as the original tumors. Cytogenetic analysis of SCC cell lines over several passages also indicated that cultured tumor cells are genetically stable (Carey et al 1989). Furthermore, karyotypes from early primary cultures and tumors are identical to those in later passages (Carey et al 1993a, 1993b; van Dyke et al 1993; Worsham 1991). p53 mutations in tumor tissue and cell lines were found to be identical (Burns et al 1993; Sakai and Tsuchida 1992; Sakai et al 1992). Studies in mouse xenografts of SCC cell lines showed that the p53 staining is retained in the resulting tumors (Caamano et al 1993; Gusterson et al 1991). Cultured OSCC cell lines thus seem to be a valid representation of in vivo tumors.

For clinical application, a fast, easy-to-use, and cost-effective method for determination of the p53 status in a given tissue sample is most desirable. It would allow identification of patients at higher risk for a less favorable course of disease in the malignant tumors or patients at a higher risk of developing cancer among those with benign precursor lesions in the oral mucosa. Immunohistochemical detection of p53 reactivity in tissue samples seems to be such a useful, simple, and rapid technique to screen

Table 9: p53 Overexpression and Mutation in Head and Neck Cancer Cell Lines

CELL LINE	IMMUN.	CODON	MUTATIONS
SCC4	+	151	C to T
SCC9	−	274–285	32 bp deletion
SCC9G	−	271	deletion
SCC25	−	208	2 bp del.
SCC35	+	273	G to A
SQ38	−	196	C to T
JSQ3	−	72 and 289	G to C and G to −
UMSCC10A	+	245	G to T
UMSCC10B	+	245	G to T
UMSCC16	+	248	G to T
UMSCC19	+/−	148–151	10 bp del.
UMSCC23	+	176	G to T
EVSCC1	+/−	213	C to T
FaDu	+	248	G to T
LICR-LON-HN5	+	238	T to A
LICR-LON-HN6Rr	+	152	C to T
Detroit 562	+	174	G to A
BICR3	+	282	G to C
BICR6	−	192	C to T
BICR7	+	151	C to A
BICR16	−	146	G to A
BICR19	−	exon 10 del.	107 bp del.
BICR22	−	exon 8/9	19 bp del.
BICR31	+	173,174	3 bp del.
BICR56	+	126–132	21 bp del.
HOC605	ND	126	C to G
HOC815	ND	205	A to G
NA	ND	220	T to C
NU	ND	exon 6, s.d.	AG/GT to AAGT
HSC2	ND	exon 6, s.d.	AG/GT to AGAT
HSC5	ND	237	G to A
TSU	ND	248	C to T
Ca922	ND	248	C to T
HSC4	ND	248	G to A
OM1	ND	266	G to A
ZA	ND	279	G to A
HOC719	ND	281	C to G
HOC313	ND	285	G to A

ND = Not Determined   s.d. = splicing donor site

for potential p53 dysfunction in OSCC. Usually wild-type p53 protein is degraded rapidly and cannot be detected by immunohistochemistry. Most p53 mutations cause conformational changes of the p53 protein, which is then stabilized, resulting in a prolonged half-life. It has therefore been assumed that detection of p53 protein by immunohistochemistry is equivalent with the presence of mutation (Lane and Benchimol 1990).

p53 expression can usually not be found in normal oral mucosa (Girod et al 1993, 1994a, 1994b, 1994c; Langdon and Partridge 1992; Ogden et al 1992; Pavelic et al 1994; Shin et al 1994; Warnakulasuriya and Johnson 1992). An exception seems to be normal mucosa directly adjacent to a malignant tumor, with 21% to 64% of the tissue showing p53 overexpression (Berner et al 1993; Shin et al 1994). These findings possibly reflect the presence of genetic alterations that have not yet led to overt histologic changes.

Several retrospective studies show that p53 expression can be detected in all preneoplastic and neoplastic stages of oral carcinogenesis. In the preneoplastic lesions, up to 56% of leukoplakia are p53 positive, as well as a few cases of oral lichen planus (Figs. 8, 10) (Table 10) (Girod et al 1993, 1994a, 1994b, 1994c; Gusterson et al 1991; Kaur et al 1994; Nishioka et al 1993; Ogden et al 1992; Pavelic et al 1994; Shin et al 1994; Warnakulasuriya and Johnson 1992). The small number of p53 positive lichen planus cases corresponds well with the rare malignant transformation that is observed clinically (Fig. 13).

Alterations of the p53 gene seem to occur at the transition from the premalignant to the malignant stage in oral carcinogenesis (Girod et al 1993; Gusterson et al 1991; Ogden et al 1992; Shin et al 1994; Warnakulasuriya and Johnson 1992). According to longitudinal studies also reported herein, the original lesions were often, but not always, p53 positive in patients who later developed OSCC from oral leukoplakia and erosive lichen planus. The malignant tumors were p53 positive (Section 4.1.4.) (Pavelic et al 1994). In OSCC the rate of p53 positive biopsy results ranges from 33% to 80% of the investigated tumors (Bourhis et al 1994; Burns et al 1993; Field et al 1991, 1992; Gasparini et al 1993; Girod et al 1993, 1994a, 1994b, 1994c; Gusterson et al 1991; Homann et al 1993; Kaur et al 1994; Langdon and Partridge 1992; Nishioka et al 1993; Ogden et al 1992; Pavelic et al 1994; Shin et al 1994; Thomas et al 1994; Warnakulasuriya and Johnson 1992; Watling et al 1992). The increase in number of positive specimens correlates with dysplasia grades, loss of differentiation, and proliferation status of the premalignant and malignant lesions (Figs. 12, 13, 20) (Table 10). Because dysplasia grade is the most important prognostic factor for development of OSCC in preneoplastic lesions and because loss of differentiation is associated with rapid growth in HNSCC, p53 changes may be an important genetic factor in the genesis of these histopathologic features in oral carcinogenesis.

One of the major advantages of immunohistologic analysis is that the architecture of the tissue analyzed is left intact, allowing the localization of the protein of interest to a specific region of the tissue specimens and to a specific cell type or cellular compartment. Because p53 is a nuclear protein, the positive reaction product is mostly observed in the nuclei, not in the cytoplasm, and varies in intensity, with some nuclei staining stronger than others. Cytoplasmic location of p53 and thus presumably inactivation of p53 function, as it has been demonstrated in mammary carcinoma, has only been reported in one study of oral lesions (Langdon and Partridge 1992; Moll et al 1992). In oral preneoplastic and neoplastic lesions, p53 staining is found only in cells of epithelial origin.

In benign oral lesions, expression of p53 is usually limited to the basal and suprabasal cell layers of the epithelium (Figs. 8, 10). In some cases p53 positive cells expand to the superficial layers (Shin et al 1994). In OSCC p53 is often found in the peripheral layers of the tumor masses in differentiated tumors (Fig. 9). The more differentiated cells are p53 negative. The expression of p53 positive cells often seems to be focal in the benign lesions as well as in the more differentiated tumors. The foci may represent different clones of cells with p53 alter-

Table 10: p53 Overexpression in the Carcinogenesis in the Mucosa of the Oropharynx and Larynx

AUTHOR	YEAR	CASES	HISTOPATHOLOGY	p53 (%)	MAb
Field	1991	73	HNSCC	67	PAb 421, 1801
Gusterson	1991	47	HNSCC	34	CM1, JG8, PAb 1801
Langdon	1992	10/4/15	Norm./Preneopl./OSCC	0/50/80	PAb 240, 421, 1801
Ogden	1992	54/37	Norm./Preneopl./OSCC	0/54	CM1
Pavelic	1992	33	HNSCC	64	PAb 1801
Warnakulasuriya	1992	5/11/13/36	Norm./Ker./Dyspl./OSCC	0/0/17/35	PAb 1801
Watling	1992	55	HNSCC	62	PAb 1801
Berner	1993	26	Norm./Dyspl./SCC (Lip)	64/100/88	CM1
Gasparini	1993	70	HNSCC	57	PAb 1801
Girod	1993	39/25/85	Hyperpl./Dyspl./OSCC	21/36/46	DO7
Matthews	1993	40	OSCC	30	PAb 1801
Nishioka	1993	20/40	Leukopl./OSCC	10/52	BP53-12
Ranasinghe	1993	5/33	Preneopl./OSCC	0/11	PAb 240, 421, 1801
Bourhis	1994	49	OSCC	47	DO7
Frank	1994	43	HNSCC	37	DO7
Gluckman	1994	82	OSCC	54	PAb 1801
Girod	1994	15/104/144	Norm./Preneopl./OSCC	0/30/47	DO7
Kaur	1994	27/32	Leukopl./OSCC	55/75	PAb 421, 1801
Pavelic	1994	357/190/466	Norm./Dyspl./HNSCC	0/56/53	PAb 1801
Shin	1994	33	Norm./Dyspl./HNSCC	21/45/45	DO7
Slootweg	1994	15	OSCC	60	BP53-12
Thomas	1994	30	OSCC	17	CM1

ations, although the impression may also be due to the fact that the slides investigated represent only a two-dimensional section through the specimens. In poorly differentiated tumors, the p53 positive cells are usually randomly distributed in the tissue specimens (Fig. 11).

Detection of p53 expression is assumed to be consistent with presence of mutation of the p53 gene in the immunohistochemical studies. In some human tumors an excellent correlation exists between immunohistochemistry and detection of mutations by molecular biology methods. Several recent studies indicate though that high levels of p53 protein may exist without mutation of the gene being present (Fig. 30) (Tables 5, 6) (Barnes et al 1992; Rubio et al 1993; Rodrigues et al 1990; Thompson et al 1992).

Cases of lung, breast, and ovarian carcinoma, astrocytoma, and OSCC have been reported that have p53 accumulation as detected by immunohistochemistry, but no mutations in exons 2 to 11 (Kupryjanczyk et al 1992; Ranasinghe et al 1993a; Thompson et al 1992). In a family of breast cancer patients, strong expression of wild-type p53 protein was found in normal tissue as well as in the tumors, further confirming that p53 mutation is not necessarily the cause of p53 protein stabilization (Barnes et al 1992). The interpretation of immunohistology data may thus be more complicated.

The basis for the aberrant overexpression of wild-type p53 is still unclear. One possible explanation would be that high levels of p53 protein accumulate in rapidly proliferating nonneoplastic and neoplastic cells exerting the tumor suppressor function of the protein (Bennett et al 1991; Mercer and Baserga 1991). In fact elevated levels of wild-type p53 are seen after exposure of oral keratinocytes and other normal cells to DNA-damaging agents (Fritsche et al 1993; Gujuluva et al 1994; Lu and Lane 1993). In a clinical study overexpression of p53 was detected in 64% of normal mucosa adjacent to lip carcinomas, possibly reflecting the accumulation of wild-type p53 in response to ultraviolet radiation (Berner et al 1993). Transfection experiments in breast cancer cell lines have shown that the cellular environment and therefore presumably gene products that act upstream or downstream of p53 play an important role in the regulation of p53 expression. p53 expression may therefore be detected in cells with an intact gene (Vojtisek and Lane 1993). Elevated levels of p53 protein, where the gene does not show a mutation in oral leukoplakia and lichen planus, could reflect a regulatory mechanism by which cell cycle arrest and apoptosis are induced in cells harboring genetic damage (Gujuluva et al 1994; Lowe et al 1993b; Yonish-Rouach et al 1991). In oral carcinogenesis p53 may thus act as a tumor suppressor by eliminating the rapidly growing premalignant cells, which may eventually show malignant transformation and endanger the organism (Morgenbesser et al 1994). Aberrant expression of wild-type p53 protein then reflects the loss of the normal growth regulatory response to the protein, and detection of p53 protein by immunohistochemistry may nevertheless have a similar meaning whether it be the wild-type or the mutant form.

In most of the immunohistochemical p53 studies in HNSCC, monoclonal antibodies (mAb) have been used that detect mutated as well as wild-type p53 (Table 10). In theory, detection of wild-type p53 could be avoided by using mutation-specific p53 monoclonal antibodies, but then the question arises how specific these antibodies are and whether all mutated proteins are detected. The pattern of staining is obviously different with different p53 monoclonal antibodies and may also depend on the type of mutation of the gene (Figs. 35, 39) (Tables 2,

3) (Bodner et al 1992; Langdon and Partridge 1992).

In human HNSCC cell lines, detection of p53 expression by immunohistochemistry correlates well with presence of mutation (Table 9). However, this does not always seem to be true for tumor specimens from OSCC (Fig. 30) (Tables 2, 3) (Burns et al 1993; Maestro et al 1992; Thomas et al 1994). In one study only 3 out of 11 tumors with strong p53 expression by immunohistochemistry had p53 mutations (Pavelic et al 1994). Furthermore, p53 deletions are present in a considerable number of the cell lines and no protein can be detected by western analysis and immunohistochemistry (Burns et al 1993; Field et al 1991; Somers et al 1992). Therefore, caution should be applied to the interpretation of p53-negative biopsy specimens, because the presence of functional protein cannot be readily assumed. If p53 expression cannot be detected in a relatively large percentage of cases by immunohistochemistry, neither can it be assumed that p53 mutation is an unimportant event in oropharyngeal carcinogenesis (Warnakulasuriya and Johnson 1992).

As does immunohistologic data, molecular biology analysis indicates that mutation of p53 is an early event in head and neck carcinogenesis, preceding invasive neoplasia. Loss of heterozygosity of p53 was already found in oral leukoplakia and in OSCC (Saranath et al 1993). Another study reported loss of p53 heterozygosity in 10 of 14 (71%) intraoral SCCs at one polymorphic restriction site in heterozygous individuals; 2 of 5 carcinomas showed LOH at a second site (Largey et al 1993). Most cell lines of HNSCC show LOH of the p53 gene. For some cell lines increased p53 hybridization has been described, possibly indicating the amplification of the gene in immortalized cell lines, but not in tumors (Yin et al 1993). Because most early lesions retain the wild-type allele, its loss seems to be associated with tumor progression and advanced stages of the disease (Boyle et al 1993).

The incidence of p53 mutations increases with the transition to invasive lesions but does not increase with advancing of the tumors, as

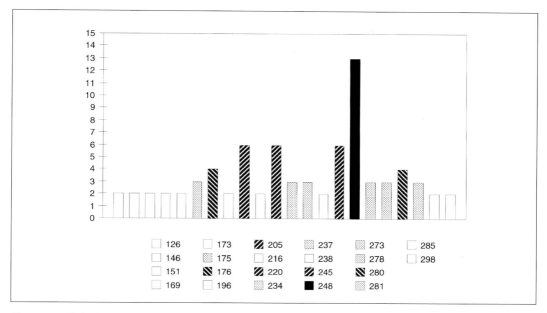

Figure 45: Point Mutations in Preneoplastic Lesions, SCC and Cell Lines from HNSCC of the Oropharynx and Larynx (No. of mutations per amino acid position)

would be expected if p53 mutations were associated with cancer progression (Boyle et al 1993; Brachman et al 1992; Chung et al 1993). In one study, 47% of the stage I and II cancers and 37% of stage III and IV cases, showed p53 mutations. Presence of p53 mutation seems to be correlated with a higher incidence of recurrence and shorter time to recurrence, suggesting that the growth advantage of p53 mutation may result in a shorter disease-free interval following treatment in head and neck cancer (Brachman et al 1992; Brennan et al 1994). The p53 mutations in OSCC show clonal fidelity for recurrent tumors and metastases (Chung et al 1993; Koch et al 1994; Pavelic et al 1994). In second primary cancers arising in patients with primary epithelial cancer of the oropharynx, the genetic lesions are discordant such that the presence or location of the mutations in the initial primary cancer differs from those of the second and third primary cancers (Chung et al 1993). Different mutations in p53

in multiple foci in the oropharyngeal mucosa may provide a molecular basis for the development of multiple tumors (Boyle et al 1993; Brachman et al 1992; Chung et al 1993; Nees et al 1993; Somers et al 1992). These observations suggest that the tumors arise as independent events and provide a molecular basis for field cancerization effects in cancers of the upper aerodigestive tract.

More than 95% of the p53 mutations in the mucosa of the oropharynx and larynx fall within exons 5 through 8, which code for the internal and most conserved part of the p53 protein (Boyle et al 1993; Brachman et al 1992; Burns et al 1993; Caamano et al 1993; Chung et al 1993; Field et al 1991; Gusterson et al 1991; Jung et al 1992; Kim et al 1993; Maestro et al 1992; Nees et al 1993; Sakai and Tsuchida 1992; Shin et al 1994; Somers et al 1992; Thomas et al 1994) (Data summarized in Fig. 45). Mutations of the p53 gene were detected in 25% to 68% of SCCs and 19% of preinvasive

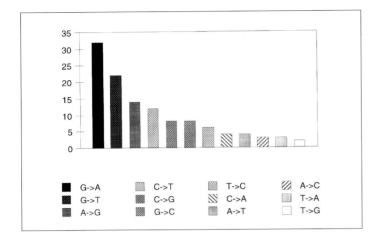

■ G->A	▨ C->T	▧ T->C	▨ A->C
■ G->T	▨ C->G	▨ C->A	▨ T->A
■ A->G	▨ G->C	▨ A->T	☐ T->G

Figure 46: Type of Point Mutation in HNSCC and Cell Lines from HNSCC (No. of mutations per base)

and severe dysplastic lesions of the head and neck, indicating a relatively good correlation with the immunohistochemistry data. In those studies where only few alterations were found using molecular biology methods, detection of p53 mutations may be obliterated by presence of nonmalignant cells, eg, stromal cells. It is therefore important to employ proper tissue preparation techniques and sequencing strategies sensitive enough to detect mutations in the presence of the remaining normal cells (Mac-Geoch et al 1991). According to the available data, codons 175 and 176, 205, 220, 234, 237, 245, 248, and 273 to 281 appear to be "hot spots" for p53 mutations in HNSCC (Boyle et al 1993; Brachman et al 1992; Burns et al 1993; Caamano et al 1993; Chung et al 1993; Field et al 1991; Gusterson et al 1991; Jung et al 1992; Kim et al 1993; Maestro et al 1992; Nees et al 1993; Sakai and Tsuchida 1992; Shin et al 1994; Somers et al 1992; Thomas et al 1994) (Fig. 45). The most frequently altered site, Arg[248], anchors p53 to the DNA minor grove with hydrogen bonds. The crystal structure of the p53 protein recently revealed that missense mutations at any point in the protein can alter p53 function because of the secondary structure of the protein (Cho et al 1994).

The type of mutation varies considerably in different kinds of human cancers, suggesting that etiologic agents may be associated with specific base changes in the DNA and may also be responsible for typical sites of mutations in the p53 gene (Hollstein et al 1994a, 1994b; Kandioler et al 1994). In head and neck cancer 83% of the p53 mutations are point mutations. Of these, 53% are at guanine nucleotides (Fig. 46). These changes are often associated with benzo-(α)-pyrenes and nitrosamines from cigarette smoke (Puisieux et al 1991; Shelby and Sancar 1993). Heavy smoking and drinking are well-recognized risk factors for OSCC, and mutations of the p53 gene may be induced by the specific carcinogens present therein. Most studies report a link between the overexpression of p53 protein or p53 mutation in carcinomas of the head and neck and a history of heavy smoking and drinking (Boyle et al 1993; Brennan et al 1994; Chung et al 1993; Field et al 1991, 1992; Langdon and Partridge 1992; Ogden et al 1992; Shin et al 1994). In one immunohistochemical study no correlation between these parameters was found (Matthews 1993). The correlation between cigarette smoking, OSCC, and p53 alterations is further supported by two studies of patients with a history of betel nut and tobacco chewing. Although the incidence of OSCC in these patients is high, p53 overexpression was only found in 11% to 17% of the tumors and the rate of p53 mutation was low (Ranasinghe et al 1993a; Thomas et al 1994). In patients with a history of betel nut chewing and tobacco chewing or smoking p53 expression was higher in preneoplastic and neoplastic lesions in comparison with other studies (Kaur et al 1994).

Cancers induced by smoking occur more often in the larynx and lung, where the inhaled smoke is concentrated, and not in the oropharynx. It has been speculated that heavy exposure to alcohol may be more closely correlated with oropharyngeal cancer (Schottenfeld 1979). The p53 mutation pattern of oral cancers alone is indeed different from all head and neck cancers and from lung cancers. In lung cancers 37% of all mutations are guanine to thymine transversions, but only 19% of head and neck cancers and 4% of oral cancers show this mutation type (Hollstein et al 1994; Thomas et al 1994). In comparison with lung cancer, the frequency of transitions in oral cancer is much higher, also indicating a difference in carcinogenic exposure (Chung et al 1993; Sakai and Tsuchida 1992). These differences in the mutational spectrum may reflect the effects of free oxygen radicals which are increased in ethanol metabolism (Khanna and Israel 1980). Nevertheless, the consistency of the type of p53 mutations in head and neck and oral cancer are compatible with exposure of these patients to common carcinogens. If the nature and site of p53 mutations reflect the mutagens involved in tumorigenesis and the capacity of malignant transformation, the characterization of p53 mutations in lichen planus, oral leukoplakia, and OSCC may provide a basis for assessing the prognosis of the patients.

Inactivation of p53 function can also occur through amplification of the MDM2 gene and binding of the protein to p53 (Momand et al 1992; Oliner et al 1992). Loss of p53 tumor suppressor function due to MDM2 amplification and overexpression has been found in tumors and cell lines deriving from sarcomas and gliomas where p53 mutations were often absent (Cordon-Cardo et al 1994; Khatib et al 1993; Leach et al 1993; Oliner et al 1992; Reifenberger et al 1993). MDM2 amplification was not detected in tumors of the upper aerodigestive tract, where p53 mutation is frequent, although by immunohistochemistry MDM2 staining was found in a high percentage of benign and malignant lung tissue specimens (Waber et al 1993; Wiethege et al 1994). In frozen sections human sarcomas MDM2 amplification has been correlated with the intensity of the MDM2 immunohistochemical nuclear staining (Leach et al 1993). In oral premalignant and malignant lesions, the number of tissue specimens with detectable nuclear MDM2 expression was in general lower than p53-positive specimens but increased also during carcinogenesis (Figs. 20, 35, 38). A mostly focal expression pattern was detected (Figs. 39). Biopsy tissues with both p53 and MDM2 nuclear staining were found in the late stages of SCC. Based on the currently available data, a possible explanation for positive staining of p53 and MDM2 in the same lesion may be that in those lesions overexpression of wild-type p53 is detected and has led to increased expression of MDM2, which can in turn inhibit its functions. According to these immunohistochemical results, further studies on the molecular level concerning the role of MDM2 in head and neck cancer should be of great importance.

5.1.2. Rb Alterations in Oral Carcinogenesis

Functional loss of the retinoblastoma gene has been found in a diverse group of human malignancies. Impairment of Rb function due to Rb mutation may also play an important role in the carcinogenesis in head and neck cancer. RB protein can be detected in human tissues using immunohistochemical techniques (Cordon-Cardo and Richon 1994). Normal tissue and tumors with normal RB protein were shown to display a mosaic pattern of staining that was easily distinguishable from the lack of staining in tumors and cell lines not expressing the RB protein (Xu et al 1991). The lack of nuclear staining in a significant portion of normal and RB positive cells corresponds to cells that are in the middle of the G0 or G1 phase of the cell cycle, where apparently the concentration of RB protein is 10 times lower than during G2-M. Surrounding stromal cells were not found to react with the antibody (Grand et al 1989; Varley et al 1989).

In nearly all the cases of oral premalignant and malignant lesions investigated for RB by immunohistochemistry, positive RB staining was detected (Figs. 23, 24, 35). The detection of RB by immunohistochemistry in paraffin-embedded tissue sections seemed to correlate well with the presence or absence of mutation. The cell line H209, in which a mutation in exon 21 was determined, was negative by immunohistochemistry, whereas the cell lines SCC 4 and SCC 15 without mutation of the Rb gene were RB positive by immunohistochemistry (Fig. 25). Presence or absence of RB protein was also confirmed by western blot (Fig. 26). DNA analysis of the tissue specimens did not reveal any mutations in the exons investigated. Loss of heterozygosity, which has a 20% chance of random occurrence in the tumors, was detected at the retinoblastoma locus in 10% of the OSCCs tested (Table 4), but in all of these cases RB protein was detected by immunohistochemistry. These observations and other studies imply that impairment of Rb function does not play an important role in oral carcinogenesis (Lee et al 1993a, 1993b; Xu et al 1991; Yoo et al 1994).

5.2. Proliferation Activity and Loss of Tumor Suppressor Gene Function as "Biomarkers" in Diagnosis and Prognosis of OSCC

The development of oral carcinoma can almost certainly be ascribed to genetic damage inflicted on cell growth regulatory genes, presumably by the known etiologic factors, eg, smoking and/or excessive consumption of alcohol. According to this idea, malignant changes in the oral mucosa are driven by the accumulation of mutations in these genes, resulting first in an increase in proliferation activity as it can be found in benign white oral lesions. The normal maturation of the oral epithelium is thus disturbed and abnormal keratinization with epithelial dysplasia occurs, as is seen eventually in premalignant lesions of the oral mucosa such as leukoplakia.

Alternatively, proliferation activity may not be induced by genetic damage; rather it is due to underlying inflammation caused by immunologic reactions, as in oral lichen planus. The increased proliferation may then render epithelial cells more susceptible to genetic damage. The risk of malignant development in these lesions is small, however, as changes at the gene level are not yet present and the cellular response to stimulating signals is regulated normally. These differences are correlated with the differences in the risk of malignant transformation in oral lichen planus and oral leukoplakia, which have been known for years. However, in both scenarios one cell can eventually sustain enough genetic damage to cell cycle regulatory genes that a growth advantage is established. Clonal growth then overgrows the surrounding cells, and eventually lack of response to negative external and internal cell growth regulatory stimuli is established, resulting in the formation of oral squamous cell carcinoma.

Most oral squamous cell carcinomas appear to consist of a multiclonal cell population with different biologic characteristics. Only a small fraction of the tumor cells may have the ability to metastasize, and the malignant potential of a tumor or benign lesion may largely depend on a small clonal population that shows aggressive growth. Ideally it should be possible to identify these cells in a given lesion and thus assess its future "biologic" behavior.

Because genetic changes accumulate during carcinogenesis and precede malignant transformation or invasion in OSCC, markers of cellular or molecular changes need to be defined that are associated with specific stages of the disease. In recent years identification of such biomarkers has become an important field of research in head and neck cancer (Huber and

Hong 1994; Lippman et al 1990; Pillai 1993; Vokes et al 1993). The expression and pattern of a biomarker should be correlated with the risk of carcinogenic transformation in benign lesions or the progression of the disease in tumors. Alterations of the marker should occur prior to malignant transformation, and the changes should be clonally preserved.

Activation of cellular oncogenes and loss of function of suppressor genes appears to be the key event in the formation of most human cancers. Altered forms of these genes or their protein products have the potential to provide a new generation of cancer markers. The most useful application of oncogenes and suppressor genes so far has been in providing prognostic information. Although oncogenes and suppressor genes have the potential to supply prognostic information in a broad range of cancers, many of the results are still preliminary with conflicting conclusions.

Mutation and thus loss of function of the p53 gene and proliferation markers such as PCNA and Ki-67 can be assessed by molecular biology methods and immunohistochemistry and are excellent candidates for biomarkers in oral carcinogenesis. Because each p53 mutation is specific for the clonal population of cells that allow tumor development in an individual case, the detection of the mutation could serve as a diagnostic marker for the presence of tumor cells not only in tissue samples, but also in body fluid, eg, saliva (Sidransky et al 1993).

5.2.1. Assessment of Proliferation Potential and Tumor Suppressor Gene Inactivation in Benign and Malignant Lesions in the Oral Mucosa

In kinetic terms tumors are believed to contain three groups of cells: proliferating cells that are involved in the cell cycle (S, G1, M, G2), non-proliferating cells in G0, and cells that have ceased to divide. In oral stratified epithelium, the basal and suprabasal cells form the proliferation pool. The total turnover time of human oral epithelium is estimated to be in the order of 10 to 14 days (Schroeder 1981). In OSCC

the growth of the tumor depends on the number of proliferating or cycling cells in the total cell population. Cell lines deriving from OSCC have lost the ability to growth arrest and terminally differentiate, two features which are usually found in normal keratinocytes (Rheinwald and Beckett 1980; Scott et al 1988). Tumor proliferation activity is thus an important predictor of biologic behavior in various malignant tumors.

Valuable methods for assessing the growth potential of OSCC today are flow cytometric DNA analysis, monoclonal antibody detection of 5'-bromodeoxyuridine (BrdU), Ki-67, proliferating cell nuclear antigen (PCNA), and the silver staining of nuclear organizer regions (AgNOR). There are limitations to each of the methods. BrdUrd can only be used in fresh or frozen sections (Sasaki et al 1986). AgNOR can assess the proliferation activity in paraffin-embedded tissue specimens (Zöller et al 1993). Counting the NORs per nucleolus is time consuming, however, and best done using a semiautomatic image analysis system. Flow cytometry requires digestion of the tissue. Therefore, the tissue architecture is lost and simultaneous histopathologic analysis of cell proliferation features cannot be performed (Böcking et al 1985; Borg et al 1992; Burgio et al 1992; Hemmer and Kreidler 1990; Kokal et al 1988; Suzuki et al 1994; Tytor et al 1990; Zöller 1993).

Immunohistochemical staining with Ki-67 and PCNA monoclonal antibodies allows simultaneous assessment of histopathologic features and the distribution of the proliferating cells. Ki-67 monoclonal antibody staining is low in G1 and increases to peak levels in cells in the G2 and M phases of the cells cycle. There is no staining of G0 cells (Hitchcock 1991). Proliferating nuclear antigen (PCNA) is an auxiliary protein of DNA polymerases δ, the principal replicative DNA polymerase, and plays an important role in DNA replication and repair during the cell cycle. The expression of PCNA in the cell cycle increases through G1, peaks at the G1-S phase and decreases in the G2 phase of the cell cycle. PCNA is undetectable during M phase and in quiescent cells. Semiquantitative analysis of positively stained cells in the tissue specimens allows a good assessment of the proliferation potential of the individual lesion with both antibodies. Although variations in the level of PCNA and problems with standardization of Ki-67 staining have been reported, all nuclei should be scored as positive regardless of staining intensity because loss of antigenicity of the protein may be due to tissue processing (Coltrera and Gown 1991; Edström et al 1991; Hitchcock 1991; Kurki et al 1988; Morris and Mathews 1989; Rijzewijk et al 1989; Scott et al 1991).

A linear correlation in proliferation activity has been found in comparison with AgNORs in OSCCs (Tsuji et al 1992a; Zöller et al 1993). PCNA and Ki-67 expression also seems to correlate well with increasing cellular atypia in oral carcinogenesis as indicated by DNA measurements (Steinbeck et al 1993; Tsuji et al 1992a; Zöller et al 1993). In one study DNA synthesis activity in the basal cell and suprabasal cell layer of oral leukoplakia was assessed using in vitro labeling with ^{3}H thymidine. In comparison with the normal mucosa DNA synthesis was higher in the basal cells in the benign leukoplakia, whereas the precancerous lesions showed a shift of activity to the suprabasal cell layer. A correlation with the grade of dysplasia could not be demonstrated however (Schell and Würth 1988).

In oral carcinogenesis the expression of the proliferation markers PCNA and Ki-67 correlates relatively well with the histopathologic classification in normal mucosa, and benign and malignant lesions in the oral mucosa (Figs. 14, 29, 36, 40) (Frerich et al 1992; Girod et al 1993, 1994a, 1994b, 1994c; Lippman et al 1990; Lorz et al 1994; Nishioka et al 1993; Schliephake et al 1992; Shin et al 1993; Slootweg et al 1994; Störkel et al 1993; Tsuji et al 1992b). A linear correlation can be observed between Ki-67 and PCNA scores. Normal mucosa exhibits low numbers of immunoreactive cells. In premalignant lesions of the oral mucosa PCNA and Ki-67 expression is already elevated in comparison with normal mucosa, and the number gradually increases with the dysplasia grade in the premalignant lesions and the loss of differentiation in the car-

cinomas, thus suggesting a higher proliferation rate in the malignant tumors (Fig. 36). Interestingly, normal epithelium of individuals who smoke and who have a malignant tumor show a much higher proliferation activity in comparison with normal mucosa from healthy nonsmokers (Shin et al 1993). The number of positive cells was found to be highly elevated also in lichen planus cases indicating a rapid proliferation of basal cells in these lesions (Figs. 14, 29) (Girod et al 1994a, 1994b, 1994c). It is clinically well known that lichen planus only rarely develops into tumors. In lichen planus the increased cell proliferation and degeneration in the basal membrane zone may be induced by the underlying lymphocytic infiltrate. T-cell-mediated immune response against a yet unknown antigen is assumed to be the major pathogenic mechanism in oral lichen planus.

In the benign lesions and in normal mucosa, PCNA and Ki-67 positive cells are found mostly in the basal cell layer. As in the human oral mucosa, DNA synthesis and cell division takes place not only in the basal cell layer but also in the suprabasal cell layer of the epithelium. PCNA and Ki-67 reactivity may also be found in the suprabasal cells (Figs. 6, 16). In differentiated tumors Ki-67- and PCNA-positive cells are found in the peripheral layers of the tumor masses in differentiated tumors and are randomly distributed in the less differentiated tumors (Figs. 7, 17). Proliferative cell clusters are often interdispersed among quiescent cells, which may represent different cancer cell clones in OSCC (Edström et al 1991; Shin et al 1993). Overall, PCNA and Ki-67 show a similar distribution pattern in normal and tumor tissue in oral carcinogenesis. The majority of the data so far accumulated suggest that although there are differences in tissue handling and scoring method, semiquantitative analysis of PCNA and Ki-67 expression in oral lesions is a reliable and easy method for assessment of the proliferation activity of an individual tissue specimen and correlates well with the histopathologic diagnosis. Assessment of proliferation activity by immunohistochemistry using these antibodies thus seems to have great potential as a biomarker.

The prognostic value of a given biomarker or diagnostic procedure should be evaluated and confirmed by means of multivariant statistic analysis. Such statistical tools can be used to analyze several factors of possible prognostic value simultaneously. The significance of a new prognostic factor can then be compared to the TNM classification in OSCC. According to the TNM classification, small and early stage tumors should have an excellent prognosis. Some small tumors show aggressive growth, however, and metastasize rapidly. This behavior seems to be associated with increased proliferation activity. PCNA and Ki-67 expression were investigated immunohistochemically in several studies in squamous cell carcinomas of the head and neck. In one study increased PCNA expression was correlated with a short survival rate in patients with OSCC (Störkel et al 1993) or identified as an indicator for malignant transformation of premalignant lesions (Reid et al 1992). In other studies, including the one reported herein, a significant correlation was observed between survival rate and Ki-67 index, but not survival rate and PCNA (Fig. 41) (Girod et al 1994a, 1994b, 1994c; Roland et al 1994; Tsuji et al 1992b). Patients with a high PCNA score in the original biopsy even seem to have a slightly better survival rate (Fig. 42).

The evidence concerning PCNA and Ki-67 expression and prognosis on oral carcinogenesis is controversial so far. The data available suggest that proliferation activity alone is not always a reliable prognostic factor for a poor prognosis as far as carcinomatous transformation, aggressive malignant growth, and development of metastases are concerned. On the contrary, the response to combination treatment of OSCC may even be preferable in rapidly proliferating tumors. Highly proliferative oral squamous cell carcinomas as determined by PCNA immunohistology have indeed been shown to have a significantly better response to radiation therapy (Günzl et al 1993). High PCNA and Ki-67 counts were also found to decrease in response to successful chemotherapeutic treatment of OSCC (Tsuji et al 1992a; Zöller 1991). Furthermore positive response to radiation treatment as measured by rapidly de-

creased Ki-67 labeling rates were related to poor clinical outcome in OSCC (Ogawa et al 1992). Thus, immunostaining with PCNA and Ki-67 monoclonal antibodies of biopsy specimens of head and neck squamous cell carcinoma before and during radiation therapy may be useful in estimating favorable response to chemotherapy and radiation therapy.

Increased proliferation activity in benign, premalignant, and malignant lesions of the oral cavity presumably reflects a series of genetic and cellular alterations. Given the current knowledge about interaction of p53, Rb and PCNA in cell cycle regulation, there are several possible ways in which control of proliferation of basal cells in the oral epithelium could be lost. Because proliferation activity alone does not necessarily indicate malignant transformation, determination of the p53 status may allow differentiation of reactive or potentially neoplastic proliferation in oral lesions.

Wild-type p53 protein has been described to negatively regulate cellular proliferation and block the cell cycle at the G1-S border. Among the genes with p53-dependent transcription is the universal cdk-inhibitor p21. In response to DNA damaging agents wild-type p53 and subsequently transcription of p21 are induced. Only recently p21 was found to exert its function by binding to proliferating nuclear antigen (PCNA) and blocking PCNA-dependent DNA replication and proliferation of the cell (Barak et al 1993; El-Deiry et al 1993; Flores-Rozas et al 1994; Harper et al 1993; Waga et al 1994; Wu et al 1993; Xiong et al 1993a, 1993b). p53 and PCNA expression were found to increase in human skin in response to ultraviolet irradiation, indicating the role of p53 and PCNA in DNA-damage repair (Hall et al 1993). This regulation pathway fails if p53 is mutated, possibly resulting in an increased proliferation rate. If p53 fails to arrest cell cycle progression after DNA damage, the propagation of DNA damage to the progenitor cells may result and malignant transformation may be promoted (reviewed in: Hartwell 1992). In oral carcinogenesis, overexpression of the p53 gene as detected by immunohistochemistry is associated with rapid tumor cell proliferation and the degree of histologic differentiation (Fig. 37) (Bourhis et al 1994; Nishioka et al 1993). In fact, cells that are positive for p53 and PCNA or Ki-67, indicative of active proliferation, display the same distribution pattern in oral lichen planus, oral leukoplakia, and OSCC (Figs. 6 to 11, 15 to 17) (Nishioka et al 1993; Girod et al 1993, 1994a, 1994b, 1994c; Lorz et al 1994; Shin et al 1993; Slootweg et al 1994; Steinbeck et al 1993). PCNA and Ki-67 reactivity can be found in all stages of oral carcinogenesis and in normal oral mucosa, whereas less than 80% of the tumors and less than 56% of the premalignant lesions show p53 expression. In addition, p53-expressing cells appear usually less frequently in the same tissue specimens. Therefore, cells overexpressing p53 represent a subset of the proliferating cells.

p53 alterations in cells that are dividing makes sense. Once the cells leave the progenitor department they are committed to differentiation, and control of cell proliferation is no longer necessary, because they do not divide. Therefore, p53 expression may not be detectable in differentiating cells even if a mutation prevails, because the gene is no longer expressed. The critical "decision" about malignancy and continuous proliferation or determination to differentiation is made at an early stage in undifferentiated progenitor epithelial cells. Malignant epithelial cells, as in OSCC, would then remain at an undifferentiated state and continue to proliferate. This is also supported by the correlation between proliferation activity and loss of differentiation in the OSCC, as determined by histopathologic analysis. In oral leukoplakia the PCNA and Ki-67 scores rise with the presence of dysplasia in the lesions, which is again indicative of a disturbed normal maturation and differentiation in the oral epithelium (Figs. 14, 29, 36, 40).

Loss of p53 function does not seem to be the only cause of increased proliferation in oral lesions, however. Higher proliferation as indicated by PCNA and Ki-67 scores is not confined to the areas where p53 expression is detectable by immunohistochemistry. Ki-67 and PCNA expression increases in p53-positive as well as p53-negative tumors (Fig. 22) (Langdon and Partridge 1992; Slootweg et al 1994; Watling et al 1992). Assuming that p53 negativity means that at least in some cases the p53 gene is normal, cells somehow seem to be able to bypass the suppressor function of the normal gene. Furthermore, proliferation rate is elevated in normal mucosa surrounding the tumors (Berner et al 1993; Shin et al 1994). Although the increased proliferation rate could be due to loss of p53 function, as indicated by immunohistochemistry, tumors also seem to elaborate factors that induce PCNA expression in nearby normal cells and PCNA induction in the normal cells surrounding tumors may be a direct example of the effect of tumor cells on normal surrounding tissues (Hall et al 1994). Nevertheless, loss of p53 function seems to be an important factor in loss of proliferation control in oral carcinogenesis, and detection of p53 expression by immunohistochemistry may have great potential as a biomarker.

Although, as a method of detecting p53 overexpression, immunohistochemistry is easy to use, standardization of the p53 data is difficult in comparison with the proliferation markers, and caution has to be applied to the interpretation of the data (Battifora 1994). First, there is the question of how representative small clinical biopsy specimens are for a given tumor or premalignant oral lesion. It has been observed in several studies that the invasive tumor front seems to be less differentiated in comparison with the superficial layers and seems to be of greater prognostic value (Bryne 1991; Hell et al 1992). p53 expression is also more likely to be found in the less differentiated cells of the invading tumor margins (Burns et al 1993; Bourhis et al 1994; Gusterson et al 1991). Because some specimens may not include these layers of the tumor, it is feasible that in a given specimen p53 overexpressing cells are not detected, although they may be present in other areas of the lesion. Furthermore, a longitudinal study revealed that in some cases tissue taken at biopsy from the same patient from different areas of the oral cavity over several years are all p53 positive by immunohistochemistry, whereas p53 expression differed in other patients. These findings suggest that different clones of cells with p53 mutations may be present in all areas of the epithelium of the upper aerodigestive tract (Nees et al 1993). Also, p53 overexpression does not necessarily pervade the tissue; very often it will be detected only in a few focal clusters in a given tumor specimen, suggesting clonal heterogeneity of the lesions (Shin et al 1994). However, intensity of p53 staining may largely depend on the tissue processing procedure employed prior to immunohistochemical staining, eg, fixation time and method (Pavelic et al 1992). Because of the nonhomogenous expression and staining pattern of p53, quantification of p53 expression as detected by immunohistochemistry may not lead to reproducible results. Therefore, in most immunohistochemical studies biopsy results were counted as either positive or negative depending on the detection of p53 expression, and no quantitative analysis was performed (Bourhis et al 1994; Burns et al 1993; Frank et al 1994; Gasparini et al 1993; Girod et al 1993, 1994a, 1994b, 1994c; Gluckman et al 1994; Gusterson et al 1991; Homann et al 1993; Matthews et al 1993; Ogden et al 1992; Pavelic et al 1992; Ranasinghe et al 1993a; Slootweg et al 1994; Watling et al 1992; Warnakulasuriya and Johnson 1992). In some studies p53 staining was scored as negative, moderate, and strong (Berner et al 1993; Field et al 1991; Kaur et al 1994; Langdon and Partridge 1992; Nishioka et al 1993; Thomas et al 1994).

Not surprisingly, the prognostic significance of p53 expression as detected by immunohistochemistry remains unclear, although several studies have been carried out in head and neck cancer. In a retrospective study described here all originating preneoplastic lesions in patients who later developed OSCC were p53 positive with one or two mAb (Table 8). Prognostic relevance could not be established, however, because of the small number of patients. Patients with a p53-positive tumor were found to have a significantly higher incidence of metastases (Gasparini et al 1993). Analysis of malignancy grading scores demonstrated strong association between p53 overexpression and high scores (Nishioka et al 1993; Watling et al 1992). In most studies, including the one described

here, comparison of the tumors that were negative for p53 with tumors that stained positive revealed no statistically significant differences with respect to the stage of disease, metastatic node involvement, size of the primary tumor, recurrence, or survival rate (Field et al 1991; Frank et al 1994; Gapany et al 1993; Pavelic et al 1992; Schipper and Kelker 1994; Warnakulasuriya and Johnson 1992).

The lack of consistent results is most likely due to problems with the standardized acquisition and preparation of the material and evaluation of the data. If p53 expression in oral lesions is used as a marker for prognosis, care has to be taken to ensure the sampling of representative biopsy material, the best possibility being the complete surgical removal and histopathologic assessment of the whole lesion. Because this is often not possible, several biopsies, especially of the invading margins, should be taken if p53 expression is evaluated. Because different monoclonal antibodies have different specificities in detecting p53 in tissue and epitopes may be destroyed by tissue processing, it may even be advisable to use at least two different antibodies. In addition, there are usually considerable interobserver variations for many clinical and diagnostic procedures, which may place patients into different prognostic groups. For the TNM classification of OSCC and also for evaluation of histopathologic features, an overall agreement of 70% between different investigators was found (Bryne et al 1989; Henk 1985). Ideally, therefore, specimens should be evaluated and graded by one investigator.

Nevertheless, analysis of p53 expression and proliferation activity could be particularly useful in small tumors and premalignant lesions. The TNM classification is widely used as a prognostic factor. Shortcomings of the predictive value of the TNM system have been noted though in clinical practice. Therefore, attempts have been made to improve the prognosis assessment by including more prognostically significant parameters (Platz et al 1986, 1988, 1992). In about 10% of the cases small tumors in early stages grow and metastasize aggressively and have a poor prognosis. It could be expected that patients with p53 alterations and a high proliferation rate show a more aggressive course of disease. Indeed, a recent retrospective analysis showed a favorable survival rate of p53-negative patients in T1 OSCC (Gluckman et al 1994). Furthermore, patients with a below-average proliferation rate (Ki-67) and no p53 in their tumors showed a significantly better survival rate than patients with an above average proliferation rate (Fig. 43). The same could not be established for PCNA, however, probably because of the small number of patients. Because p53 changes occur early in oral carcinogenesis, immunohistochemical determination of p53 alteration and increased proliferation seems to be a good tool to identify patients with a less-favorable prognosis in OSCC. In the future immunohistochemical analysis may be supported by mutational analysis of tumor tissue and margins using mutation specific probes that can greatly facilitate the molecular analysis.

5.2.2. Detection of Anti-p53 Antibodies as Circulating Markers in OSCC

Diagnosis of occult disease and monitoring of OSCC therapy may also greatly be improved by the detection of specific circulating biologic markers for the disease. There are several markers that have been investigated in head and neck cancer, including oral squamous cell carcinoma. These include oncofetal protein, enzymes, hormones, immune parameters, lipids, oncolipids and gangliosides, viral markers, tumor associated antigens, prostaglandins and prostacyclins, and base elements. So far no single marker has been identified that is not limited by lack of sensitivity and specificity (reviewed in: Rassekh et al 1994). Sensitivity and accuracy are still limited but are higher if combination assays with different markers are used. It appears from all the data collected so far that sialic acid is the most sensitive marker for SCC, followed by SCC antigen and ferritin. Recent work has shown that a combination assay with CEA (carcinoembryonic antigen), SCCA (SCC antigen), and IAP (immunosuppressive acidic protein) may be useful for screening patients with oral cancer (Kurokawa et al 1993). Because of the limited specificity, circulating markers are not widely used clinically today. In the future, the development of new multiple marker assays may be useful for clinical application.

Because a high percentage of OSCC contain conformationally changed p53 protein, detection of anti-p53 response may be a useful marker in diagnosis and follow-up of OSCC patients. In general, mutant proteins can be considered foreign and become targets for a humoral immune response. Studies using monoclonal antibodies, however, showed that mutant p53 protein does not have a dominant antigenic epitope (Labrecque et al 1993; Matlashewski et al 1986; Schlichtholz et al 1992). Nevertheless, about 12% of cancer patients contain p53-antibodies in their serum, whereas no anti-p53 antibodies were detected in 164 healthy individuals (Crawford et al 1984). The highest prevalence of anti-p53 antibodies was associated with B-cell lymphoma (21%), and ovarian and colon cancers (15%), followed by lung (8%) and breast (5%) cancers (Angelopoulou et al 1994; de Fromentel et al 1987; Labreque et al 1993; Matlashewski et al 1986; Schlichtholz et al 1992). One recent investigation reported that 50% of patients with p53 mutations were found to make p53 antibodies (Couch et al 1994). The anti-p53 response in tumor patients is most likely not induced by the mutations associated with the conformational changes of the protein. Rather it may result from loss of tolerance due to the massive release of p53 in necrotizing tumors.

Recently an immunoassay (ELISA) for detection of anti-p53 antibodies in patient serum has been described and tested in a wide variety of human cancers. In OSCC 18% of the patients were found to have anti-p53 antibodies. Immunohistochemistry indicated that the tumors contained high levels of mutant p53. As p53 antibodies were found mostly in advanced disease, the stage and degree of tumor necrosis seem to be important for the immune response in OSCC. Sequential analysis also showed that the p53-antibody test may have potential for patient monitoring. The measurement of p53 antibodies seems to be a relatively specific serologic test for cancer, which can be performed with easily automatable and quantitative methodologies. Immunoassays are simpler and more cost-efficient than DNA-based assays, which means they have an excellent potential for clinical use. These assays could potentially serve as tumor markers for recurrence during follow-up of OSCC patients.

5.3. Genetic Changes in Oral Carcinogenesis— Implications for Therapy

5.3.1. Loss of p53 Function and Multimodality Treatment of OSCC

Multimodal therapy of OSCC today is based on three pillars: surgery, radiotherapy, and chemotherapy. The rationale for surgery is obviously the removal of the tumor, while chemotherapy as well as radiotherapy are much more unspecified in their approach. Although all three therapeutic options should theoretically kill all malignant cells, the large number of treatment failures proves the contrary and therefore major questions remain.

Surgery of OSCC and premalignant lesions has been revolutionized in the last two decades by the use of lasers and the introduction of microvascular surgery that allows free flap transfer for functional reconstruction of larger defects. The radical surgical removal of the diseased tissue is assessed postoperatively by histopathologic investigation of the tumor margins. Depending on the results, the implementation of further therapy, eg, resection or postoperative radiation, is evaluated. Histopathologic examination of the normal margins of OSCC usually reveals uniformly marked epithelial hyperplasia and hyperkeratosis of the surrounding epithelium.

The inclusion of molecular biology techniques in the pathologic diagnosis of surgical and biopsy specimens from OSCC and benign precursor lesions could greatly improve the detection of changes not yet apparent by microscopy and allow for a more radical therapy in cases with widespread genetic alterations of the oral mucosa. Immunohistochemical investigations as well as recent studies using molecular biology methods such as the polymerase chain reaction technique (PCR) have demonstrated alterations of the tumor suppressor gene p53 in tumor margins and chromosomal changes that were disease-free by light microscopy (Saranath et al 1994; Voravud et al 1993). Furthermore, p53 mutations found in the tumor margins detected by PCR were highly predictive of recurrence (Mao et al 1994). At the moment, the molecular biology techniques required for these investigations are still very time-consuming and tedious, limiting the application of these improved diagnostic procedures in a clinical setting. It is feasible, however, that improvement of existing protocols or development of new automated techniques for the detection of mutations will make routine application in the clinical care for oral cancer patients possible in the near future. The clinical and histopathologic staging as well as the follow-up could thus be greatly improved in patients carrying specific mutations of the p53 gene and provide a more accurate prediction of tumor recurrence. The detection of recurrence should become possible at a much earlier stage, and additional therapeutic options could be employed earlier.

The detection of mutations in clinically and histopathologically "normal" mucosa also leads to several important conclusions for the therapy of OSCC. First, genetic damage may be more widely spread in the oral mucosa than histopathologic changes in the epithelium indicate. Second, in accordance with the concept of field cancerization, genetic damage of the oral mucosa may be extensive, and complete removal by surgery may be virtually impossible (Fig. 21) (Table 2) (Nees et al 1993). Surgery alone, therefore, cannot be successful in most cases of OSCC and even in oral leukoplakia, because malignant cells escape removal and detection by the currently used diagnostic methods, especially when occult metastases in the locoregional lymph nodes are involved. Despite a radical surgical approach, local recurrences and locoregional metastases are the major reason for treatment failure in OSCC. The detection of widespread molecular changes in the oral mucosa thus provides the rationale for combination therapy in OSCC, which has proven successful in the past.

During the last decades since combined modality treatments have been introduced into oral cancer therapy, the survival rate has not improved much further. Increasingly aggressive variations in combination treatment, including surgery, radiotherapy, and chemotherapy, did not change the poor prognosis of OSCC, but severe side effects became more apparent that negatively influence quality of life and ultimately the survival of OSCC patients. Using molecular biology techniques, it should be possible in the near future to identify those patients at high risk of developing recurrence due to widespread disease or the accumulation of genetic changes that are connected with a more aggressive behavior in benign and premalignant lesions of the oral mucosa. These selected patients could then profit from a more aggressive treatment approach using the currently available therapeutic options, and the overall survival rate may thereby improve.

5.3.2. Cell Cycle Control, Therapy, and Prevention of OSCC

The challenge in cancer therapy today is the identification and exploitation of regulatory weaknesses of cancer cells, using specifically tailored therapeutic regimen (reviewed in: Gibbs and Oliff 1994). Radiation therapy as well as chemotherapy in OSCC are limited because of their effects on other dividing cells in the human body, such as the mucosal lining of the gastrointestinal tract, including the oropharynx, and the hematopoetic system. Furthermore, although good overall response rates to initial treatment can be achieved, in most cases of OSCC neither chemotherapy nor radiation therapy are sufficient for curing the disease. There is also a wide variation in the response to those therapies. A large percentage of OSCCs do not seem to be particularly susceptible to radiation or chemotherapy. In fact, failure to respond to radiation or chemotherapeutic treatment and the development of tumors with resistant cell populations upon relapse are major impediments to successful therapy in patients with OSCC. The information about cancer therapeutics and their effects on molecules and reactions that control cell proliferation is accumulating fast. Although a coherent picture about the interactions of these processes has not yet emerged, some prospects for cancer therapy seem to be in sight.

The majority of clinically effective anticancer drugs that are available today inhibit some aspect of the machinery responsible for DNA replication and chromosome segregation. Drug action also arrests cells at defined points in the cell cycle called checkpoints. These checkpoints ensure that subsequent cell cycle events are inhibited until the inflicted damage is repaired. The fidelity of checkpoint control and susceptibility of cells to apoptosis while repair is occurring may be important factors in the success of chemotherapy (O'Connor and Kohn 1992). Despite the recent advances in the understanding of cellular responses to DNA-damaging agents the initial targets of ultraviolet or ionizing radiation are still unclear (reviewed in: Herrlich and Rahmsdorf 1994). The understanding of cellular response to DNA damage provides the rationale for some of the mechanisms by which OSCC cells, as any other tumor cells, might lose sensitivity to cytotoxic treatments and eventually develop resistance (Fisher 1994; Kohn et al 1994; O'Connor and Kohn 1992; Smets 1994).

In general, chemotherapeutic agents and radiation exert their effects on growing cells by blocking DNA replication, damaging DNA, or interfering with chromosome segregation. Recent investigations suggest that mutations of the p53 tumor suppressor gene are involved in this process and may account for some of the therapeutic failures (Lowe et al 1993a, 1993b). Normally p53 functions to prevent the expansion of cells with genetic damage by mediating cell cycle arrest in G1 to allow for repair of DNA damage or by inducing apoptosis in these cells. Loss of the tumor suppressor gene function allows cells to continue to proliferate and accumulate genetic damage. It has been hypothesized that tumor cells lacking the p53 checkpoint function are likely to be more sensitive to cell killing by radiation because these cells enter S phase despite unrepaired DNA damage. In human SCC, differences in radiation sensitivity also seem to reflect alterations in DNA repair (Dulic et al 1994; Maity et al 1994; Schwartz et al 1994). It has recently been shown, however, that the p53 tumor suppressor gene is required for the efficient activation of apoptosis (Lowe et al 1993a). Therefore, cells lacking functional p53 may display resistance to radiation and chemotherapeutic treatment (McIlwrath et al 1994; Kohn et al 1994). Because up to 80% of OSCCs harbor mutations of the p53 tumor suppressor gene, inactivation of the gene might be an important determinant of the efficacy of today's multimodal OSCC therapy protocols. Successful strategies for radiation therapy may well need to take into account the tissue of origin and the status of p53 in the tumor. In HNSCC cell lines no association between radiosensitivity and p53 mutation has been noted (Brachman et al 1993; Jung et al 1992). However, high resistance of the cell line SCC4, which is known to harbor mutant p53, to ultraviolet irradiation has been reported (Gujuluva et al 1994).

A further important conclusion from these data could be that in patients with extended lesions of the oral cavity, eg, in OSCC arising from preneoplastic lesions such as leukoplakia, radiation or chemotherapy might lead to accumulated DNA damage in preneoplastic cells, where p53 function is already lost. Because DNA damage is not repaired and apoptosis not induced because of lack of p53, these cells might acquire the necessary genetic "hits" for malignant transformation. In fact it is clinically well known that patients with excessive leukoplakia lesions and recurring small carcinomas

in different areas can be managed by surgery alone for a long time, until one of the lesions shows explosive growth and resistance to combined therapeutic treatment. The concept of multistep carcinogenesis provides the rationale for this clinical observation, namely that over time enough genetic damage is acquired to escape growth control and therapeutic control, which might be connected especially with damage of the p53 gene.

Therapy resistance thus seems to be largely due to the genotype of the tumor, which cannot be influenced today. Though it has been shown that drug resistance in cells lacking p53 can be overcome by higher doses in vitro, this strategy is limited in vivo because of the severe side effects of chemotherapeutic agents (Kaufman et al 1989; Lennon et al 1991; Sen and D'Incalci 1992). Cytotoxic treatment of p53-deficient tumors may even have adverse effects, as cells are likely to acquire further mutations because of loss of adequate repair of DNA damage (Kastan et al 1992; Lane 1992). The resulting cell clone may explain the growth potential and treatment resistance of recurrent tumors in OSCC, which can be observed clinically. Locoregional recurrences of OSCC in general do not respond well to further cytotoxic therapy, with surgery being left as the only modestly successful treatment modality in these cases. Not surprisingly, locoregional recurrence is the major cause of death in OSCC. In general, tumor cells seem to have weaker feedback controls than normal cells. Inhibitors of feedback controls could thus abolish these controls in tumor cells with little effect on normal cells and greatly enhance the efficacy of chemotherapy or radiation therapy in OSCC. Identification of potent inhibitors of cell cycle-dependent kinases (CDI), eg, p21 and p16, has opened intriguing new perspectives in drug development for cancer therapy. Compounds that activate CDIs may selectively interrupt cell cycle progression in tumor cells where the p53 tumor suppressor gene is inactivated. Because a large number of oral cancers and preneoplastic lesions contain p53 mutation, this could be a potentially powerful new way of treatment or prevention of malignant development. It has also been shown that caffeine, which keeps cells with DNA damage from entering mitosis, increases the number of tumor cells killed in tissue culture experiments and in animals (Murray 1992).

A considerable volume of studies suggest retinoids and related compounds as agents for the treatment of oral leukoplakia and prevention of head and neck cancer. Low dietary intake or serum levels of β-carotenes are associated with increased risk of various epithelial malignancies (Lippman et al 1987; Peto et al 1981; Sporn et al 1976). In a number of non-randomized clinical trials with vitamin A as well as β-carotene clinical remissions of oral leukoplakia in up to 90% have been reported (Garewal et al 1990, 1993, 1994; Malaker et al 1991; Stich et al 1985, 1988). During the last 20 years retinoids, especially all-trans RA, 13-cis-retinoic acid and etretinate, have been used successfully in the systemic treatment of oral leukoplakia (Hong et al 1986; reviewed in: Huber and Hong 1994). Recent results showed that retinoids can decrease the number of second primary tumors in patients with squamous cell carcinoma of the head and neck, and several clinical studies concerning chemoprevention in head and neck cancer are still under way (Huber and Hong 1994; de Vries et al 1992). According to preliminary data reported by Huber and Hong (1994), p53 status and thus cell-cycle control may also play an important role in the therapeutic response to retinoids. Patients with normal p53 respond to retinoid treatment, whereas those with p53 mutations do not respond.

Reintroduction of genes into damaged cells, also known as gene therapy, is currently in an experimental stage, but holds great promises for cancer therapy in the future. In animal experiments, after introduction of a recombinant adenoviral vector containing wild-type p53 in head and neck cancer cell lines, the cells went into growth arrest and apoptosis. Nude mice with established squamous cell carcinoma where the vector was injected around the tumor nodules showed significant reduction in size. Since introduction of wild-type p53 into these cell lines attenuated their replication and tumor growth, it may be feasible to develop adenoviral vectors as a potential novel therapeutic agent for OSCC (Liu et al 1994).

6. Summary

Squamous cell carcinomas of the oropharnyx account for 1%–4% of all cancers in the United States and Europe today, and the incidence has been rapidly increasing more than 50% during the last decades. Oral cancer is a disease of the elderly and is closely connected with cigarette smoking and alcohol consumption. Since the successful introduction of multimodal treatment, the survival rate of approximately 45% has not changed. Because of the high mortality and potentially disfiguring treatment, today's efforts are aimed at eliminating risk factors, chemoprevention, improvement in diagnostic procedures, and understanding of the genetic mechanisms of oral carcinogenesis.

Immunohistochemical and molecular biology analysis of biopsy tissue and cell lines of pre-neoplastic and neoplastic lesions originating from the oral mucosa have shown that alterations of the p53 tumor suppressor gene, but not of the Rb gene, play an important role in oral carcinogenesis. Wild-type p53 mediates cell cycle arrest, allowing for repair of damaged DNA, or cell death, by interacting with proteins of the cell cycle machinery.

In oral carcinogenesis inactivation of p53 function and loss of proliferation control occurs mostly as a result of mutations. Of p53 mutations in head and neck cancer 83% are point mutations, and of these 53% are at guanine nucleotides. Codons 175, 176, 205, 220, 234, 237, 245, 248, and 273 to 281 appear to be "hot spots" for p53 mutations. Specific changes reflect the mutagens involved in oral cancer, especially cigarette smoking and consumption of alcohol. Because mutations are discordant in second primary tumors and between distant sites of the mucosa, they provide the molecular basis for "field cancerization" in the upper aerodigestive tract. Other mechanisms for p53 inactivation in oral cancer that seem to be of lesser importance include binding to the E6 viral oncoprotein of HPV and interaction with the MDM2 gene.

The data on p53 alterations support the concept of multistep oral carcinogenesis and suggests the following sequence for p53 alterations: (1) p53 mutation in oral epithelial cells due to common carcinogens, eg, cigarette smoking and/or drinking ("initiation" step); (2) increased proliferation and clonal expansion, possibly associated with development of overt histopathologic changes (dysplasia of the epithelium) ("promotion"); (3) aquisition of further genetic damage, including deletion of the wild-type p53 allele leading to invasive oral cancer. It thus seems to be feasible to indentify patients with a higher risk of an unfavorable course of disease by assessing the p53 status in the oral lesions.

Mutations af the p53 gene can be detected using molecular biology methods and immunohistochemistry, as conformational changes of the protein lead to a prolonged half-life of the protein. Immunohistochemistry is an easily used method that has been employed in a number of studies, in which p53 overexpression has been detected in up to 56% of oral leukoplakia and lichen planus and in 33% to 80% of oral cancers. Because the architecture of the tissue analyzed is left intact, p53 expression could be localized to the proliferating cells of epithelial origin in oral lesions. p53 positive cells are often detected in clusters, especially in the invading tumor margins, and may not be evenly distributed in the tissue samples. Therefore, great care has to be taken to include the tumor margins in the biopsy specimens for immunohistochemical analysis. Several studies have also shown that p53 overexpression is not necessarily correlated with presence of gene mutation. Overexpression of wild-type p53 may reflect the physiologic response of a genetically healthy cell to DNA damage. Standardization and interpretation of the immunohistochemical data is therefore difficult and ideally should be reconfirmed by molecular analysis.

Statistical analysis of immunhistochemical data did not identify significant and consistent differences of p53 expression with respect to the stage of disease, malignant transformation, metastatic node involvement, recurrence, or survival rate in most studies. Nevertheless, p53 overexpression seems to be strongly correlated with histologic progression of the disease, thus confirming the importance of p53 alterations in oral carcinogenesis. Immunohistochemical and molecular analysis of the p53 status appear to be especially useful in the histopathologic assessment of the tumor-free margins of surgical specimens of OSCC. Several studies have shown that p53 alterations found in histologically "normal" tissue surrounding the tumors are highly predictive for recurrence in OSCC patients. In fact, because of the influence of common carcinogens, genetic damage may be extensive in the oropharynx, even if the mucosa appears to be unaltered. Surgery alone cannot be sufficient to remove all genetically altered cells; it has to be supplemented by other treatment modalities such as radiation and chemotherapy, which have been employed successfully in the treatment of OSCC.

Overexpression of p53 is usually found in the less differentiated, proliferating cells in benign and malignant oral lesions, thus reflecting the important role of p53 in cell cycle regulation. Assessment of the proliferating activity has become possible by immunohistochemical staining with monoclonal antibodies against PCNA and Ki-67. Statistical analysis showed that overexpression of p53 in combination with a high proliferation rate is prognostically significant for a less favorable course of disease in OSCC. All patients in the study were treated with the same therapeutic regimen consisting of radiation, chemotherapy, and radical surgery; therefore, these findings are likely to reflect an unfavorable response to therapy. Resistance of the human OSCC to radiation and chemotherapy may be linked to presence of mutant p53 or absence of wild-type p53 protein, as it is indicated by the detection of p53 overexpression in these patients. As p53 cannot function normally the proliferation rate of the cells in the tumors is elevated, as determined by PCNA and Ki-67, and the response to radiation and chemotherapy is impaired. Normally, if p53 is intact, cells should stop proliferating or undergo apoptosis in response to DNA damage. These response pathways may be altered in the tumors that harbor a p53 mutation, resulting in therapy resistance and a clinically more aggressive course of the disease. Therefore, p53 status may have to be taken into account in the therapy of OSCC in the future.

Analysis at the molecular level has confirmed important parts of the model of oral carcinogenesis as it is outlined above, although there is still a lot of work to be done. Most importantly, premalignant lesions of OSCC already harbor the same genetic changes as OSCC, and mutations found in primary tumors are identical with those of their metastases. It is obvious already that a more detailed understanding of the basic principles of oral carcinogenesis and the application of molecular biology techniques in the diagnosis of the disease and patient follow-up will be of great importance for the future development of new and more successful therapeutic strategies in oral premalignancies and cancer.

7. Bibliography

Abramova, E.J.: Lichen ruber planus der Mundhöhle. Dermatol. Wochenschr. 154, 315–323 (1968).

Ajchenbaum, F., Ando, K., DeCaprio, J.A., Griffin, J.D.: Independent regulation of human D-type cyclin gene expression during G1 phase in primary human T lymphocytes. J. Biol. Chem. 268, 4113– 4119 (1993).

Akasu, R., From, L., Kahn, H.J.: Lymphocyte and macrophage subsets in active and inactive lesions of lichen planus. Am. J. Dermatopathol. 15, 217–223 (1993).

Almendral, J.M., Huebsch, D., Blundell, P.A., MacDonald-Bravo, H., Bravo, R.: Cloning and sequence of the human nuclear protein cyclin: Homology with DNA-binding proteins. Proc. Natl. Acad. Sci. USA 84, 1575–1579 (1987).

Altman, J., Perry, H.O.: The variations and course of lichen planus. Arch. Dermatol. 84, 47–59 (1961).

Anderson, J.A., Irish, J.C., McLachlin, C.M., Ngan, B.Y.: H-ras oncogene mutation and human papillomavirus infection in oral carcinomas. Arch. Otolaryngol. Head Neck Surg. 120, 755–760 (1994).

Andreasen, J.O.: Oral lichen planus: I. A clinical evaluation of 115 cases. Oral Surg. Oral Med. Oral Pathol. 25, 31–42 (1968).

Andreasen, J.O.: Oral lichen planus II. A histologic evaluation of ninety-seven cases. Oral Surg. Oral Med. Oral Pathol. 25, 158–166 (1968).

Andreasson, L., Björlin, G., Korsgaard, R., Matthiason, J., Trell, E.: Karzinome und Leukoplakien im Mundhöhlenbereich im Verhältnis zu AHH-Induktion, Rauchen und Zahnstatus. HNO 32, 112–114 (1984).

Angelopoulou, K., Diamandis, E.P., Sutherland, D.J., Kellen, J.A., Bunting, P.S.: Prevalence of serum antibodies against the p53 tumor suppressor gene protein in various cancers. Int. J. Cancer 58, 480–487 (1994).

Anneroth, G., Batsakis, J., Luna, M.: Review of the literature and a recommended system of malignancy grading on oral squamous cell carcinomas. Scand. J. Dent. Res. 95, 229–249 (1987).

Atkinson, L., Chester, I.C., Smyth, F.G., Seldam R.E.: Oral cancer in New Guinea: A study in demography and etiology. Cancer 17, 1289–1298 (1964).

Austyn, J.: The dendritic cell system and anti-tumour immunity. in vivo 7, 193–202 (1993).

Axéll, T., Holmstrup, P., Kramer, I.R., Pindborg, J.J., Shear, M.: International seminar on oral leukoplakia and associated lesions related to tobacco habits. Community Dent. Oral Epidemiol. 12, 145–154 (1984).

Axéll, T., Rundquist, L.: Oral lichen planus—a demographic study. Community Dent. Oral Epidemiol. 15, 52–56 (1987).

Axéll, T.: A prevalence study of oral mucosal lesions in an adult Swedish population. Odont. Revy 27, Suppl. 36 (1976).

Bandara, L.R., Buck, V.M., Zamanian, M., Johnston, L.H., La Thangue, N.B.: Functional synergy between DP-1 and E2F-1 in the cell cycle-regulating transcription factor DRTF1/E2F. EMBO J. 12, 4317–4324 (1993).

Banks, L., Matlashewski, G., Crawford, L.: Isolation of human-p53-specific monoclonal antibodies and their use in the studies of p53 expression. Eur. J. Biochem. 739, 529–534 (1986).

Bánóczy, J., Csiba, Á.: Comparative study of the clinical picture and histopathologic structure of oral leukoplakia. Cancer 29, 1230–1234 (1972).

Barak, Y., Juven, T., Haffner, R., Oren, M.: mdm2 expression is induced by wild type p53 activity. EMBO J. 12, 461–468 (1993).

Barbosa, M.S., Edmonds, C., Fisher, C., Schiller, J.T., Lowy, D.R., Vousden, K.H.: The region of HPV E7 oncoprotein homologous to adenovirus E1a and SV40 large T antigen contains separate domains for Rb binding and casein kinase II phosphorylation. EMBO 9,153–160 (1990).

Barch, D.H., Walloch, J., Hedvegi, D., Iannacone, P.M.: Histopathology of methylbenzylnitrosamine-induced esophageal carcinoma in the rat: Comparison with cytomorphology. J. Natl. Cancer Inst. 77, 1145–1153 (1986).

Barnard, N.A., Scully, C., Eveson, J.W., Cunnigham, S., Porter, S.R.: Oral cancer development in patients with oral lichen planus. J. Oral Pathol. Med. 22, 421–424 (1993).

Barnes, D.M., Hanby, A.M., Gillett, C.E., Mohammed, S., Hodgson, S., Bobrow, L.G., Leigh, I.M., Purkis, T., MacGeoch, C., Spurr, N.K., Bartek, J., Vojtesek, B., Picksley, S.M., Lane, D.P.: Abnormal expression of wild type p53 protein in normal cells of a cancer family patient. Lancet 340, 259–263 (1992).

Battifora, H.: p53 immunhistochemistry: A word of caution. Human Pathol. 25, 435–437 (1994).

Becker, J.: Neue Aspekte zur Immunpathogenese des oralen Lichen planus. Dtsch. Zahnärztl. Z. 47, 872–874 (1992) (English abstract).

Becker, Y.: Dendritic cell activity against primary tumors: An overview. in vivo 7, 187–192 (1993).

Benedict, W.F, Murphree, A.L., Banerjee, A., Spina, C.A., Sparkes, M.C., Sparkes, R.S.: Patient with 13 chromosome deletion: Evidence that the retinoblastoma gene is a recessive cancer gene. Science 219, 973–975 (1983).

Bennett, W.P., Hollstein, M.C., He, A., Zhu, S.M., Resau, J.H., Trump, B.F., Metcalf, R.A., Welsh, J.A., Midglay, C., Lane, D.P., Harris, C.C.: Archival analysis of p53 genetic and protein alterations in Chinese esophageal cancer. Oncogene 6, 1779– 1784 (1991).

Berner, A., Holm, R., Naess, A., Hjortdal, O.: p53 protein expression in squamocellular carcinomas of the lip. Anticancer Res. 13, 2421–2424 (1993).

Birch, J.M., Hartley, A.L., Tricker, K.J., Prosser, J., Condie, A., Kelsey, A.M., Harris, M., Jones, P.H., Binchy, A., Crowther, D., Craft, A.W., Eden, O.B., Evans, D.G., Thompson, E., Mann, J.R., Martin, J., Mitchell, E.L., Santibánez-Koref, M.F.: Prevalence and diversity of constitutional mutations in the p53 gene among 21 Li-Fraumeni families. Cancer Res. 54, 1298–1304 (1994).

Böcking, A., Auffermann, W., Vogel, H., Schlöndorff, G., Goebbels, R.: Diagnosis and grading of malignancy in squamous epithelial lesions of the larynx with DNA cytophotometry. Cancer 56, 1600–1604 (1985).

Bodner, S.M., Minna, J.D., Jensen, S.M., D'Amico, D., Carbone, D., Mitsudomi, T., Fedorko, J., Buchhagen, D.L., Nau, M.M., Gazdar, A.F., Linnoila, R.I.: Expression of mutant p53 proteins in lung cancer correlates with the class of p53 gene mutation. Oncogene 7, 743–749 (1992).

Bodrug, S.E., Warner, B.J., Bath, M.L., Lindeman, G.J., Harris, A.W., Adams, J.M.: Cyclin D1 transgene impedes lymphocyte maturation and collaborates in lymphogenesis with the myc gene. EMBO 13, 2124–2130 (1994).

Boisnic, S., Frances, C., Branchet, M.-C., Szpirglas, H., Le Charpentier, Y.: Immunohistological study of oral lesions of lichen planus: Diagnostic and pathophysiologic aspects. Oral Surg. Oral Med. Oral Pathol. 70, 462–465 (1990).

Bookstein, R., Shew, J.Y., Chen, P.L., Scully, P., Lee, W.H.: Suppression of tumorigenicity of human prostate carcinoma cells by replacing a mutated RB gene. Science 247, 712–715 (1990).

Borg, B., Klebe, H.-W., Neugebauer, W., Steinbeck, R.: DNA-Gehalt von Plattenepithelkarzinomen des Mundbodens und der Lippe sowie von oralen Dysplasien. Dtsch Z. Mund Kiefer Gesichtschir. 16, 102–105 (1992).

Borges, A.M., Shrikhande, S.S., Ganesh, B.: Surgical pathology of squamous carcinoma of the oral cavity: Its impact on management. Semin. Surg. Oncol. 5, 310–317 (1989).

Boring, C.C., Squires, T.S., Tong, T.: Cancer Statistics. CA Cancer J. Clin. 43, 7–26 (1993).

Bouquot, J.E., Gorlin, R.J.: Leukoplakia, lichen planus, and other oral keratoses in 23,616 white Americans over the age of 35 years. Oral Surg. Oral Med. Oral Pathol. 61, 373–381 (1986).

Bouquot, J.E., Whitaker S.B.: Oral leukoplakia—rationale for diagnosis and prognosis of its clinical subtypes or "phases". Quintessence Int. 25, 133–140 (1994).

Bourhis, J., Bosq, J., Wilson, G.D., Bressac, B., Talbot, M., Leridant, A.M., Dendale, R., Janin, N., Armand, J.P., Luboinski, B., Malaise, E.P., Wibault, P., Eschwege, F.: Correlation between p53 gene expression and tumor-cell proliferation in oropharyngeal cancer. Int. J. Cancer 57, 458–462 (1994).

Boyd, A.S., Neldner, K.H.: Lichen planus. J. Am. Acad. Derma. 25, 593–619 (1991).

Boyle, J.O., Hakim, J., Koch, W., van der Riet, P., Hruban, R.H., Roa, R.A., Correo, R., Eby, Y.J., Ruppert, J.M., Sidransky, D.: The incidence of p53 mutations increases with the progression of head and neck cancer. Cancer Res. 53, 4477–4480 (1993).

Boysen, M., Loven, J.O.: Second malignant neoplasms in patients with head and neck squamous cell carcinomas. Acta Oncol. 32, 283–288 (1993).

Brachman, D.G., Beckett, M., Graves, D., Haraf, D., Vokes, E., Weichselbaum, R.R.: p53 mutation does not correlate with radiosensitivity in 24 head and neck cancer cell lines. Cancer Res. 53, 3667–3669 (1993).

Brachman, D.G., Graves, D., Vokes, E., Beckett, M., Haraf, D., Montag, A., Dunphy, E., Mick, R., Yandell, D., Weichselbaum, R.R.: Occurrence of p53 gene deletions and human papilloma virus infection in human head and neck cancer. Cancer Res. 52, 4832–4836 (1992).

Brandt, B., Greger, V., Yandell, D., Passarge, E., Horsthemke, B.: A simple and non-radioactive method for detecting the Rbl.20 polymorphism in the retinoblastoma gene. Am. J. Hum. Genet. 51, 1450–1451 (1992).

Bravo, R., Frank, R., Blundell, P.A., MacDonald-Bravo, H.: Cyclin/PCNA is the auxiliary protein of DNA polymerase-delta. Nature 326, 515–517 (1987).

Bréchot, C.: Oncogenic activation of cyclin A. Curr. Opin. Genet. Dev. 3, 11–18 (1993).

Brennan, J.A., Boyle, J.O., Koch, W.M., Hruban, R.H., Couch, M.J., Eby, Y.J., Forastiere, A., Sidransky, D.: Effect of p53 mutations on survival in head and neck squamous cell carcinoma. Head Neck 16, 510 (1994).

Brenner, L., Munoz-Antonia, T., Vellucci, V.F., Zhou, Z.L., Reiss, M.: Wild-type p53 tumor suppressor gene restores differentiation of human squamous carcinoma cells but not the response to transforming growth factor beta. Cell Growth Differ. 4, 993–1004 (1993).

Bricker, S.L.: Oral lichen planus: A review. Semin. Dermatol. 13, 87–90 (1994).

Brown, D.R., Deb, S., Munoz, R.M., Subler, M.A., Deb, S.P.: The tumor suppressor p53 and the oncoprotein siman virus 40 T antigen bind to overlapping domains on the mdm2 protein. Mol. Cell. Biol. 13, 6849–6857 (1993).

Brown, R.S., Bottomley, W.K., Abramovitch, K., Langlais, R.P.: Immediate biopsy versus a therapeutic trial in the diagnosis and treatment of oral vesiculobullous / vesiculoerosive oral lesions: Opposing viewpoints presented. Oral Surg. Oral Med. Oral Pathol. 73, 694–697 (1992).

Brown, R.S., Bottomley, W.K., Puente, E., Lavigne, G.L.: A retrospective evaluation of 193 patients with oral lichen planus. J. Oral Pathol. Med. 22, 69–72 (1993).

Bruszt, P.: Stomato-onkologische Reihenuntersuchungen in sieben Gemeinden Südungarns. Schweiz. Monatsschr. Zahnheilkd. 72, 758–766 (1962).

Bryne, M., Koppang, H.S., Lilleng, R., Stene, T., Bang, G., Dabelsteen, E.: New malignancy grading is a better prognostic indicator than Broders' grading in oral squamous cell carcinomas. J. Oral Pathol. Med. 18, 432–437 (1989).

Bryne, M.: Prognostic value of various molecular and cellular features in oral squamous cell carcinomas. J. Oral Pathol. Med. 20, 413–420 (1991).

Bschorer, R., Frerich, B., Gehrke, G., Sachse, R., Gärtner, H.-V., Schwenzer, N.: Orale Leukoplakien – eine histopathologische und retrospektive Studie. Dtsch. Zahn-Mund-Kieferheilkd. 80, 347–350 (1992).

Buchkovich, K., Duffy, L.A., Harlow, E.: The retinoblastoma protein is phosphorylated during specific phases of the cell cycle. Cell 58, 1097– 1105 (1989).

Buckley, M.F., Sweeney, K.J., Hamilton, J.A., Sini, R.L., Manning, D.L., Nicholson, R.I., de Fazio, A., Watts, C.K., Musgrove, E.A., Sutherland, R.L.: Expression and amplification of cyclin genes in human breast cancer. Oncogene 8, 2127–2133 (1993).

Burgio, D.L., Jacobs, J.R., Maciorowski, Z., Del Mar Alonso, M., Pietraszkiewicz, H., Ensley, J.F.: DNA ploidy of primary and metastatic squamous cell head and neck cancers. Arch. Otolaryng. Head Neck Surg. 118, 185–187 (1992).

Burkhardt, A., Maerker, R., Löning, T., Seifert, G.: Dysplasieklassifikation oraler Leukoplakien und Präkanzerosen. Definition und praktische Anwendung. Dtsch. Z. Mund- Kiefer- Gesichtschir. 2, 221–231 (1978). (english abstract)

Burkhardt, A., Maerker, R.: Dysplasieklassifikation oraler Leukoplakien und Präkanzerosen. Bedeutung für Prognose und Therapie. Dtsch. Z. Mund- Kiefer-Gesichtschir. 2, 199–205 (1978). (english abstract)

Burkhardt, A., Maerker, R.: Vor- und Frühstadien des Mundhöhlenkarzinoms. Carl Hanser Verlag München/Wien 1981.

Burkhardt, A.: Advanced methods in the evaluation of premalignant lesions and carcinomas of the oral mucosa. J. Oral. Pathol. 14, 751–778 (1985).

Burns, J.E., Baird, M.C., Clark, L.J., Burns, P.A., Edington, K., Chapman, C., Mitchell, R., Robertson, G., Soutar, D., Parkinson, E.K.: Gene mutations and increased levels of p53 protein in human squamous cell carcinomas and their cell lines. Br. J. Cancer 67, 1274–1284 (1993).

Byers, R.M: Squamous cell carcinoma of the oral tongue in patients less than thirty years of age. Am. J. Surg. 130, 475–478 (1975).

Caamano, J., Zhang, S.Y., Rosvold, E.A., Bauer, B., Klein-Szanto, A.G.: p53 alterations in human squamous cell carcinoma and carcinoma cell lines. Am. J. Pathol. 142, 1131–1139 (1993).

Cairns, J.: Cancer: Science and society. W.H. Freeman New York 1978.

Cairns, P., Mao, L., Merlo, A., Lee, D.J., Schwab, D., Eby, Y., Tokino, K., van der Riet, P., Blaugrund, J.E., Sindransky, D.: Rates of p16 (MTS1) mutations in primary tumors with 9p loss. Science 265, 415–416 (1994).

Callender, T., El-Naggar, A.K., Lee, M.S., Frankenthaler, R., Luna, M.A., Batsakis, J.G.: PRAD-1 (CCND1) / cyclin D1 oncogene amplification in primary head and neck squamous cell carcinoma. Cancer 74, 152–158 (1994).

Carey, T.E., van Dyke, D.L., Worsham, M.J., Bradford, C.R., Babu, V.R., Schwartz, D.R., Hsu, S., Baker, S.R.: Characterization of human laryngeal primary and metastatic squamous cell carcinoma cell lines UM-SCC-17A and UM-SCC-17B. Cancer Res. 49, 6098–6107 (1989).

Carey, T.E., van Dyke, D.L., Worsham, M.J.: Nonrandom chromosome aberrations and clonal populations in head and neck cancer. Anticancer Res. 13, 2561–2568 (1993a).

Carey, T.E., Worsham, M.J., van Dyke, D.L.: Chromosomomal biomarkers in the clonal evolution of head and neck squamous neoplasia. J. Cell. Biochem. Suppl. 17F, 213–222 (1993b).

Carey, T.E.: Establishment of epidermoid carcinoma cell lines. In: Wittes, R.E. (ed.): Head and Neck Cancer. John Wiley & Sons Chichester/New York/ Brisbane/Toronto/Singapore 1985, pp 287–314.

Carter, R.L.: Pathology of squamous carcinomas of the head and neck. Curr. Opin. Oncol. 5, 491–495 (1993).

Cavenee, W.K., Dryja, T.P., Phillips, R.A., Benedict, W.F., Godbout, R., Gallie, B.L., Murphree, A.L., Strong, L.C., White, R.L.: Expression of recessive alleles by chromosomal mechanisms in retinoblastoma. Nature 305, 779–784 (1983).

Cawson, R.A.: Treatment of oral lichen planus with betamethasone. Br. Med. J. 1, 86–89 (1968).

Cepek, K.L., Shaw, S.K., Parker, S.M., Russell, G.J., Morrow, J.S., Rimm, D.L., Brenner, M.B.: Adhesion between epithelial cells and T lymphocytes by E-cadherin and $\alpha^E\beta_7$ integrin. Nature 372, 190–192 (1994).

Cesarman, E., Liu, Y.F., Knowles, D.M.: The MDM2 oncogene is rarely amplified in human lymphoid tumors and does not correlate with p53 gene expression. Int. J. Cancer 56, 457–458 (1994).

Chang, Y.-S., Lin, Y.-J., Tsai, C.-N., Shu, C.-H., Tsai, M.-S., Choo, K.-B., Liu, S.-T.: Detection of mutations in the p53 gene in human head and neck carcinomas by single strand conformation polymorphism analysis. Cancer Letters 67, 167–174 (1992).

Chen, C.Y., Oliner, J.D., Zhan, Q., Fornace, A.J. Jr., Vogelstein, B., Kastan, M.B.: Interactions between p53 and MDM2 in a mammalian cell cycle checkpoint pathway. Proc. Natl. Acad. Sci. USA 29, 2684–2688 (1994).

Chen, P.-L., Scully, P., Shew, J.-Y., Wang, J.Y., Lee, W.-H.: Phosphorylation of the retinoblastoma gene product is modulated during the cell cycle and cellular differentiation. Cell 58, 1193–1198 (1989).

Cheng, J., Scully, P., Shew, J.-Y., Lee, W.-H., Vila, V., Hass, M.: Homozygous deletion of the retinoblastoma gene in an acute lymphoblastic leukemia (T) cell line. Blood 75, 730–735 (1990).

Chiesa, F., Boracchi, P., Tradati, N., Rossi, N., Costa, L., Giardini, R., Marazza, M., Zurrida, S.: Risk of preneoplastic and neoplastic events in operated oral leukoplakias. Eur. J. Cancer Oral Onc. 29B, 23–28 (1993).

Cho, Y., Gorina, S., Jeffrey, P.D., Pavlevitch, N.P.: Crystal structure of a p53 tumor suppressor-DNA complex: Understanding tumorigenic mutations. Science 265, 346–355 (1994).

Chumakov, P.M., Jenkins, J.R.: BstNI / NciI polymorphism of the human p53 gene. Nucl. Acid Res. 19, 6969 (1991).

Clarke, A.R., Purdie, C.A., Harrison, D.J., Morris, R.G., Bird, C.C., Hooper, M.L., Wyllie, A.H.: Thymocyte apoptosis induced by p53-dependent and independent pathways. Nature 362, 849–852 (1993).

Clore, G.M., Omochinski, J.G., Sakaguchi, K., Zambrano, N., Sakamoto, H., Appella, E., Gronenborn, A.M.: High-resolution structure of the oligomerization domain of p53 by multidimensional NMR. Science 265, 386–391 (1994).

Cook, J.W., Hieger, I., Kennaway, E.L., Mayneord, W.V.: The production of cancer by pure hydrocarbons. Proc. Roy. Soc. B 111, 455–496 (1932).

Cooke, B.E.: Leukoplakia buccalis. Ann. Roy. Coll. Surg. Engl. 34, 370–383 (1964).

Cordon-Cardo, C., Latres, E., Drobnjak, M., Oliva, M.R., Pollack, D., Woodruff, J.M., Marechal, V., Chen, J., Brennan, M.F., Levine, A.J.: Molecular abnormalities of mdm2 and p53 genes in adult soft tissue sarcomas. Cancer Res. 54, 794–799 (1994).

Cordon-Cardo, C., Richon, V.M.: Expression of the Retinoblastoma Protein is regulated in normal human tissues. Am. J. Path. 144, 500–510 (1994).

Couch, M.J., Koch, W.M., Brennan, J.A., Sidransky, D.: The humoral response to p53 oncoprotein in head and neck patients. Head Neck 16, 495 (1994).

Cowan, J.M., Beckett, M.A., Ahmed-Swan, S., Weichselbaum, R.R.: Cytogenetic evidence of the multistep origin of head and neck squamous cell carcinoma. J. Natl. Cancer Inst. 84, 793–797 (1992).

Cox, M., Maitland, N., Scully, C.: Human herpes simplex-1 and papillomavirus type 16 homologous DNA sequences in normal, potentially malignant and malignant oral mucosa. Eur. J. Cancer Oral Oncol. 29B, 215–219 (1993).

Crawford, L.V., Pim, D.C., Lamb, P.: The cellular protein p53 in human tumours. Mol. Biol. Med. 2, 261–272 (1984).

Creath, C.J., Cutter, G., Bradley, D.H., Wright, J.T.: Oral leukoplakia and adolescent smokeless tobacco use. Oral Surg. Oral Med. Oral Pathol. 72, 35–41 (1991).

Cruchley, A.T., Williams, D.M., Farthing, P.M., Lesch, C.A., Squier, C.A.: Regional variation in Langerhans cell distribution and density in normal human oral mucosa determined using monoclonal antibodies against CD1, HLADR, HLADQ and HLADP. J. Oral Pathol. Med. 18, 510–516 (1989).

de Fromentel, C.C., May-Levin, F., Mouriesse, H., Lemerle, J., Chandrasekaran, K., May, P.: Presence of circulating antibodies angainst cellular protein p53 in a notable proportion of children with B-cell lymphoma. Int. J. Cancer 39, 185–189 (1987).

de Panfilis, G., Manara, G., Ferrari, C., Manfredi, G., Allegra, F.: Imbalance in phenotypic expression of T cell subpopulations during different evolutional stages of lichen planus lesions. Acta Derm. Venereol. (Stockh.) 63, 369–375 (1984).

de Villiers, E.-M.: Papilloma viruses in cancers and papillomas of the aerodigestive tract. Biomed. Pharmacother. 43, 31–36 (1989).

de Vries, N., van Zandwijk, N., Pastorino, U.: Chemoprevention in the management of oral cancer: EUROSCAN and other studies. Eur. J. Cancer Oral Oncol. 28B, 153–157 (1992).

DeCaprio, J. A., Ludlow, J. W., Lynch, D., Furukawa, Y., Griffin, J., Piwnica-Worms, H., Huang, C.-M., Livingston, D.M.: The product of the retinoblastoma susceptibility gene has properties of a cell cycle regulatory element. Cell 58, 1085–1095 (1989).

DeCaprio, J.A., Ludlow, J.W., Figge, J., Shew, J.-Y., Huang, C.-M., Lee, W.-H., Marsilio, E., Paucha, E., Livingston, D.M.: SV40 large tumor antigen forms a specific complex with the product of the retinoblastoma susceptibility gene. Cell 54, 275–283 (1988).

Dechaume, M., Payen, J., Piriou, Mme.: Le lichen plan isolé de la muqueuse buccale: Considérations anatomo-cliniques d'après 50 observations dont 30 avec examen histologique. Presse Méd. 94, 2133–2135 (1957).

Decker, J., Goldstein, J.C.: Risk factors in head and neck cancer. N. Engl. J. Med. 19, 1151–1155 (1982).

Devoto, S.H., Mudryj, M., Pines, J., Hunter, T., Nevins, J.R.: A cyclin A-protein kinase complex possesses sequence-specific DNA binding activity: p33^{cdk2} is a component of the E2F-Cyclin A complex. Cell 68, 167–176 (1992).

Di Leonardo, A., Linke, S.P., Clarkin, K., Wahl, G.M.: DNA damge triggers a prolonged p53-dependent G1 arrest and long-term induction of Cip1 in normal human fibroblasts. Genes Dev. 8, 2540–2551 (1994).

Diller, L., Kassel, J., Nelson, C.E., Gryka, M.A., Litwak, G., Gebhardt, M., Bressac, B., Ozturk, M., Baker, S.J., Vogelstein, B., Friend, S.H.: p53 functions as a cell cycle control protein in osteosarcomas. Mol. Cell. Biol. 10, 5772-5781 (1990).

Dixon, W. (ed.): BMDP statistical software manual. University of California Press Berkeley 1992.

Dontenwill, W., Chevalier, H.-J., Harke, H.-P., Klimisch, H.-J., Kuhnigk, C., Reckzeh, G., Schneider, B.: Untersuchungen über den Effekt der chronischen Zigarettenrauchinhalation beim syrischen Goldhamster und über die Bedeutung des Vitamin A auf die bei Berauchung gefundenen Organveränderungen. Z. Krebsforsch. Klin. Onkol. 89, 153-180 (1977).

Dony, C., Kessel, M., Gruss, P.: Post-transcriptional control of myc and p53 expression during differentiation of the embryonal carcinoma cell line F9. Nature 317, 636–639 (1985).

Downer, C.S., Speight P.M.: E-cadherin expression in normal, hyperplastic and malignant oral epithelium. Eur. J. Cancer Oral Oncol. 29B, 303–305 (1993).

Dryja, T.P., Cavenee, W., White, R., Rapaport, J.M., Petersen, R., Albert, D.M., Bruns, G.A.: Homozygosity of chromosome 13 in retinoblastoma. N. Engl. J. Med. 310, 550–553 (1984).

Dulic, V., Kaufmann, W.K., Wilson, S.J., Tlsty, T.D., Lees, E., Harper, J.W., Elledge, S.J., Reed, S.I.: p53-dependent inhibition of cyclin-dependent kinase activities in human fibroblasts during radiation-induced G1 arrest. Cell 76, 1013–1023 (1994).

Dunsche, A., Kreusch, T., Sauer, M.: Die Leukoplakie der Mundschleimhaut – eine retrospektive Studie and 161 Patienten. Dtsch. Zahnärztl. Z. 47, 869–871 (1992). (English abstract)

Dynlacht, B.D., Flores, O., Lees, J.A., Harlow, E.: Differential regulation of E2F trans-activation by cyclin / cdk2 complexes. Genes Dev. 8, 1772–1786 (1994).

Dyson, N., Buchkovich, K., Whyte, P., Harlow, E.: The cellular 107K protein that binds to adenovirus E1A also associates with the large T antigens of SV40 and JC virus. Cell 58, 249–255 (1989).

Eckardt, A.: Clinical impact of synchronous and metachronous malignancies in patients with oral cancer. Int. J. Oral Maxillofac. Surg. 22, 282–284 (1993).

Edström, S.S., Gustafsson, B., Stenman, G., Lydén, E., Stein, H., Westin, T.: Proliferative pattern of head and neck cancer. Am. J. Surg. 162, 412–416 (1991).

Eisenberg, E., Krutchkoff, D.J.: Lichenoid lesion of the oral mucosa: Diagnostic criteria and their importance in the alleged relationship to oral cancer. Oral Surg. Oral Med. Oral Pathol. 73, 699–704 (1992).

El-Deiry, W.S., Harper, J.W., O'Connor, P.M., Velculescu, V.E., Canman, C.E., Jackman, J., Pietenpol, J.A., Burrell, M., Hill, D.E., Wang, Y., Wiman, K.G., Mercer, W.E., Kastan, M.B., Kohn, K.W., Elledge, S.J., Kinzler, K.W., Vogelstein, B.: WAF1 / CIP1 is induced in p53-mediated G₁ arrest and apoptosis. Cancer Res. 54, 1169–1174 (1994).

El-Deiry, W.S., Tokino, T., Velculescu, V.E., Levy, D.B., Parsons, R., Trent, J.M., Lin, D., Mercer, W.E., Kinzler, K.W., Vogelstein, B.: WAF1, a potential mediator of p53 suppression. Cell 75, 817–825 (1993).

El-Labban, N.G., Kramer, I.R.: Civatte bodies and the actively dividing epithelial cells in oral lichen planus. Br. J. Dermatol. 90, 13–23 (1974).

Elledge, S.J., Harper, J.W.: Cdk inhibitors: On the threshold of checkpoints and development. Curr. Opin. Cell Biol. 6, 847–852 (1994).

Eufinger, H., Bremerich, A., Zahn, W.: Leukoplakische Veränderungen der Mundschleimhaut. Klinische und histopathologische Aspekte. Dtsch. Zahnärztl. Z. 47, 865–867 (1992). (English abstract)

Eversole, L.R., Sapp, J.P.: c-myc oncoprotein expression in oral precancerous and early cancerous lesions. Eur. J. Cancer Oral Oncol. 29B, 131–135 (1993).

Eversole, L.R.: Review of the literature. In: Millard, H.D., Mason, D.K. (eds.): World Workshop on Oral Medicine. Year Book Medical Publisher Chicago 1989, pp 54–121.

Ewen, M.E., Faha, B., Harlow, E., Livingston, D.M.: Interaction of p107 with cyclin A independent of complex formation with viral oncoproteins. Science 255, 85–90 (1992).

Ewen, M.E., Sluss, H.K., Sherr, C.J., Matsushime, H., Kato, J., Livingston, D.M.: Functional interactions of the retinoblastoma protein with mammalian D-type cyclins. Cell 73, 487–497 (1993).

Faha, B., Ewen, M.E., Tsai, L.H., Livingston, D.M., Harlow, E.: Interaction between human cyclin A and adenovirus E1A-associated p107 protein. Science 255, 87–90 (1992).

Fakharzadeh, S.S., Trusko, S.P., George, D.L.: Tumorigenic potential associated with enhanced expression of a gene that is amplified in a mouse tumor cell line. EMBO J. 10, 1565–1569 (1991).

Fang, F., Newport, J.W.: Evidence that the G1-S and G2-M transitions are controlled by different cdc2 proteins in higher eukaryotes. Cell 66, 731–742 (1991).

Faraci, R.P., Schour, L., Graykowski, E.A.: Squamous cell carcinoma of the oral cavitiy—chronic oral ulcerative disease as a possible etiologic factor. J. Surg. Oncol. 7, 21–26 (1975).

Farber, E.: The multistep nature of cancer development. Cancer Res. 44, 4217–4223 (1984).

Farmer, G., Bargonetti, J., Zhu, H., Friedman, P., Prywes, R., Prives, C.: Wild-type p53 activates transcription in vitro. Nature 358, 83–86 (1992).

Fearon, E.R., Vogelstein, B.: A genetic model for colorectal tumorigenesis. Cell 61, 759–767 (1990).

Field, J.K., Pavelic, Z.P., Spandidos, D.A., Stambrock, P.J., Jones, A.S., Gluckman, J.L.: The role of the p53 tumor suppressor gene in squamous cell carcinoma of the head and neck. Arch. Otolaryngol. Head Neck Surg. 119, 1118–1122 (1993).

Field, J.K., Spandidos, D.A., Malliri, A., Gosney, J.R., Yiagnisis, M., Stell, P.M.: Elevated p53 expression correlates with a history of heavy smoking in squamous cell carcinoma of the head and neck. Br. J. Cancer 64, 573–577 (1991).

Field, J.K.: Oncogenes and tumor-suppressor genes in squamous cell carcinoma of the head and neck. Eur. J. Cancer Oral Oncol. 28B, 67–76 (1992).

Fijuth, J., Mazeron, J.J., Le Pechoux, C., Piedbois, P., Martin, M., Haddad, E., Calitchi, E., Pierquin, B., Le Bourgeois, J.P.: Second head and neck cancers following radiation therapy of T1 and T2 cancers of the oral cavity and oropharynx. Int. J. Radiat. Oncol. Biol. Phys. 24, 59–64 (1992).

Finlay, C.A.: The mdm-2 oncogene can overcome wild-type p53 suppression of transformed cell growth. Mol. Cell. Biol. 13, 301–306 (1993).

Firpo, E.J., Koff, A., Solomon, M.J., Roberts, J.M.: Inactivation of a Cdk2 inhibitor during interleukin 2—induced proliferation of human T lymphocytes. Mol. Cell. Biol. 14, 4889–4901 (1994).

Fisher, D.E.: Apoptosis in cancer therapy: Crossing the threshold. Cell 78, 539–542 (1994).

Flores-Rozas, H., Kelman, Z., Dean, F.B., Pan, Z.Q., Harper, J.W., Elledge, S.J., O'Donnell, M., Hurwitz, J.: Cdk-interacting protein 1 directly binds with proliferating cell nuclear antigen and inhibits DNA replication catalyzed by the DNA polymerase delta holoenzyme. Proc. Natl. Acad. Sci. USA 91, 8655–8659 (1994).

Forlen, H.P., Hornstein, O., Stüttgen, G.: Betelkauen und Leukoplakie. Arch. Klin. Exper. Dermatol. 221, 463–480 (1965).

Fornace, A.J. Jr.: Mammalian genes induced by radiation: Activation of genes associated with growth control. Annu. Rev. Genet. 26, 507–526 (1992).

Frerich, B., Bschorer, R., Gehrker, G., Gärtner, H.V., Schwenzer, N.: Maligne Transformation oraler Leukoplakien. Eine retrospektive klinische und zellproliferationskinetische Studie. Dtsch. Zahnärztl. Z. 47, 836–839 (1992). (English abstract)

Friend, S.H., Bernards, R., Rogelj, S., Weinberg, R.A., Rapaport, J.M., Albert, D.M., Dryja, T.P.: A human DNA segment with properties of the gene that predisposes to retinoblastoma and osteosarcoma. Nature 323, 643–646 (1986).

Friend, S.H., Horowitz, J.M., Gerber, M.R., Wang, X.-F., Bogenmann, E., Li, F.P., Weinberg, R.A.: Deletions of a DNA sequence in retinoblastomas and mesenchymal tumors: Organization of the sequence and its encoded protein. Proc. Natl. Acad. Sci. USA 84, 9059–9063 (1987).

Fritsche, M., Haessler, C., Brander, G.: Induction of nuclear accumulation of the tumor-suppressor protein p53 by DNA-damaging agents. Oncogene 8, 307–318 (1993).

Fulling, H.-J.: Cancer development in oral lichen planus. Arch. Derm. 108, 667 (1973).

Fung, Y.-K., Murphree, A.L., T'Ang, A., Qian, J., Hinrichs, S.H., Benedict, W.F.: Structural evidence for the authenticity of the human retinoblastoma gene. Science 236, 1657–1659 (1987).

Funk, W.D., Pak, D.T., Karas, R.H., Wright, W.E., Shay, J.W.: A transcriptionally active DNA-binding site for human p53 protein complexes. Mol. Cell. Biol. 12, 2866–2871 (1992).

Gabriel, S.A., Jenson, A.B., Hartmann, D., Bottomley, W.K.: Lichen planus: Possible mechanisms of pathogenesis. J. Oral Med. 40, 56–59 (1985).

Gangadharan, P., Paymaster, J.C.: Leukoplakia—an epidemiologic study of 1504 cases observed at the Tata Memorial Hospital, Bombay, India. Br. J. Cancer 25, 657–668 (1971).

Gapany, M., Pavelic, Z.P., Gapany, S.R., Pavelic, L., Li, Y.G., Craven, J.M., Jones, H., Biddinger, P., Stambrook, P.J., Gluckman, J.L.: Relationship between immunohistochemically detectable p53 protein and prognostic factors in head and neck tumors. Cancer Detect. Prev. 17, 379–386 (1993).

Garewal, H.: Chemoprevention of oral cancer: Beta-carotene and vitamin E in leukoplakia. Eur. J. Cancer Prev. 3, 101–107 (1994).

Garewal, H.S., Meyskens, F., Friedman, S., Alberts, D., Ramsey, L.: Oral cancer prevention: The case for carotenoids and anti-oxidant nutrients. Preventive Med. 22, 701–711 (1993).

Garewal, H.S., Meyskens, F.L., Killen, D., Reeves, D., Kiersch, T.A., Elletson, H., Stroberg, A., King, D., Steinbronn, K.: Response of oral leukoplakia to beta-carotene. J. Clin. Onc. 8, 1715–1720 (1990).

Gasparini, G., Weidner, N., Maluta, S., Pozza, F., Boracchi, P., Mezzetti, M., Testolin, A., Bevilacqua, P.: Intratumoral microvessel density and p53 protein: Correlation with metastasis in head-and-neck squamous-cell carcinoma. Int. J. Cancer 55, 739–744 (1993).

Gassenmaier, A.: Papillomvirus-DNA (HPV) in leukoplakischen und kanzerösen Mundschleimhautveränderungen. Dtsch. Z. Mund Kiefer GesichtsChir. 12, 149–151 (1988).

Gawkrodger, D.J., Stephenson, T.J., Thomas, S.E.: Squamous cell carcinoma complicating lichen planus: A clinico-pathological study of three cases. Dermatology 188, 36–39 (1994).

Gerdes, J., Lemke, H., Baisch, H., Wacker, H.-H., Schwab, U., Stein, H.: Cell cycle analysis of a cell proliferation-associated human nuclear antigen defined by the monoclonal antibody Ki-67. J. Immun. 133, 1710–1715 (1984).

Gerry, R.G., Smith, S.T., Calton, M.L.: The oral charactistics of Guamians including the effects of betel chewing on the oral tissues. Oral Surg. Oral Med. Oral Pathol. 5, 762–781 (1952).

Gerson, S.J.: Oral Cancer. Oral Biol. Med. 1, 153–166 (1990).

Gibbs, J.B., Oliff, A.: Pharmaceutical research in molecular oncology. Cell 79, 193–198 (1994).

Girard, F., Strausfeld, U., Fernandez, A., Lamb, N.J.: Cyclin A is required for the onset of DNA replication in mammalian fibroblasts. Cell 67, 1169–1179 (1991).

Girod, S.C., Fischer, U., Knüfermann, R., Krämer, Ch., Krüger, G.R.F.: p53-Mutationen bei Leukoplakien, Lichen planus und Karzinomen der Mundschleimhaut. Dtsch. Z. Mund Kiefer GesichtsChir. 18, 250–253 (1994a). (english abstract)

Girod, S.C., Gerlach, K.-L., Groth, W., Feaux de Lacroix, W.: Zur Malignisierung des Lichen ruber mucosae nach Retinoidtherapie. Dtsch. Zahnärztl. Z. 47, 875–877 (1992).

Girod, S.C., Knüfermann, R., Krämer, Ch., Krüger, G.R.F.: p53 Expression in the Carcinogenesis in the Oral Mucosa. J. Cell Biochem. 56, 444–448 (1994b).

Girod, S.C., Krueger, G.R.F., Pape, H.-D.: p53 and Ki67 expression in preneoplastic and neoplastic lesions of the oral mucosa. Int. J. Oral Maxillofac. Surg. 22, 285–288 (1993).

Girod, S.C., Kühnast, T., Ulrich, S., Krueger, G.R.F.: Langerhans cells in epithelial tumors and benign lesions of the oropharynx. in vivo 8, 543–548 (1994d).

Girod, S.C., Pape, H.-D., Krueger G.R.F.: p53 and PCNA expression in carcinogenesis of the oropharyngeal mucosa. Eur. J. Cancer Oral Oncol. 30B, 419–423 (1994c).

Gluckman, J.L., Stambrook, P.J., Pavelic, Z.P.: Prognostic significance of p53 protein accumulation in early stage T1 oral cavity cancer. Eur. J. Cancer Oral Oncol. 30B, 281 (1994).

Godbout, R., Dryja, T.P., Squire, J., Gallie, B.L., Phillips, R.A.: Somatic inactivation of genes on chromosome 13 is a common event in retinoblastoma. Nature 304, 451–453 (1983).

Goodrich, D.W., Wang, N.P., Qian, Y.-W., Lee, E.Y.-H., Lee, W.-H.: The retinoblastoma gene product regulates progression through the G1 phase of the cell cycle. Cell 67, 293–302 (1991).

Graham, S., Dayal, H., Rohrer, T., Swanson, M., Sultz, H., Shedd, D., Fischman, S.: Dentition, diet, tobacco, and alcohol in the epidemiology of oral cancer. J. Natl. Cancer Inst. 59, 1611–1616 (1977).

Grand, R.J., Byrd, P.J., Grabham, P.W., Gregory, C.D., Huen, D.S., Merrick, R.M., Young, L.S., Gallimore, P.H.: The expression of the retinoblastoma gene product Rb1 in primary and adenovirus-transformed human cells. Oncogene 4, 1291–1298 (1989).

Gräßel-Pietrusky, R., Hornstein, O.P.: Histologische Klassifikation oraler Präkanzerosen. Dtsch. Z. Mund Kiefer GesichtsChir. 6, 343–351 (1982).

Gujuluva, C.N., Baek, J.-H., Shin, K.-H., Cherrick, H.M., Park, N.-H.: Effect of UV-irradiation on cell cycle, viability and the expression of p53, gadd153 and gadd45 genes in normal and HPV-immortalized human oral keratinocytes. Oncogene 9, 1819–1827 (1994).

Gundlach, K.K.: Wieviele Plattenepithelkarzinome der Mundhöhle sind aus Leukoplakien entstanden? Dtsch. Z. Mund Kiefer GesichtsChir. 16, 109–111 (1992).

Günzl, H.-J., Horn, H., Schücke, R., Donath, K.: Prognostic value of PCNA and cytokeratins for radiation therapy of oral squamous cell carcinoma. Eur. J. Cancer Oral Oncol. 29B, 141–145 (1993).

Gusterson, B.A., Anbazhagan, R., Warren, W., Midgely, C., Lane, D.P., O'Hare, M., Stamps, A., Carter, R., Jayatilake, H.: Expression of p53 in premalignant and malignant squamous epithelium. Oncogene 6, 1785–1789 (1991).

Hall, P.A., Coates, P.J., Goodlad, R.A., Hart, I.R., Lane, D.P.: Proliferating cell nuclear antigen expression in non-cycling cells may be induced by growth factors in vivo. Br. J. Cancer 70, 244–247 (1994).

Hall, P.A., McKee, P.H., du P. Menage, H., Dover, R., Lane, D.P.: High levels of p53 protein in UV-irradiated normal human skin. Oncogene 8, 203–207 (1993).

Hallopeau, M.H.: Sur un cas de lichen de Wilson gingival avec néoplasie voisine dans la région maxillaire. Bull. Soc. Fr. Dermatol. Syphigr. 17, 32 (1910).

Hannon, G.J., Beach, D.: p15^{INK4B} is a potential effector of TGF—induced cell cycle arrest. Nature 371, 257–261 (1994).

Harbour, J.W., Lai, S.-L., Whang-Peng, J., Gazdar, A.F., Minna, J.D., Kaye, F.J.: Abnormalities in structure and expression of the human retinoblastoma gene in SCLC. Science 241, 353–357 (1988).

Harland, C.C., Phipps, A.R., Marsden, R.A., Holden, C.A.: Squamous cell carcinoma complicating lichen planus of the lip. J. Roy. Soc. Med. 85, 235–236 (1992).

Harper, J.W., Adami, G.R., Wei, N., Keyomarsi, K., Elledge, S.J.: The p21 cdk-interacting protein Cip1 is a potent inhibitor of G1 cyclin-dependant kinases. Cell 75, 805–816 (1993).

Hartwell, L.: Defects in a cell cycle checkpoint may be responsible for the genomic instability of cancer cells. Cell 71, 543–546 (1992).

Hausamen, J.-E.: Tasks and objectives of the German-Austrian-Swiss working group on tumours in the maxillo-facial region (DÖSAK). Int. J. Oral Maxillofac. Surg. 17, 264–266 (1988).

Hedrum, A., Pontén, F., Ren, Z., Lundeberg, J., Pontén, J., Uhlén, M.: Sequence-based analysis of the human p53 gene based on microdissection of tumor biopsy samples. BioTechniques 17, 118–129 (1994).

Hell, B., Hinkeldey, K., Cichos, A.: Hat die Invasionsform Einfluß auf das biologische Verhalten von Mundhöhlenkarzinomen? Dtsch. Z. Mund Kiefer Gesichts Chir. 16, 95–101 (1992).

Helm, T.N., Camisa, C., Liu, A.Y., Valenzuela, R., Bergfeld, W.F.: Lichen planus associated with neoplasia: A cell-mediated immune response to tumor antigens? J. Am. Acad. Dermatol. 30, 219–224 (1994).

Hemmer, J., Kreidler, J.: Flow cytometric DNA ploidy analysis of squamous cell carcinoma of the oral cavity. Cancer 66, 317–320 (1990).

Henderson, D.S., Banga, S.S., Grigliatti, T.A., Boyd, J.A.: Mutagen sensitivity and suppression of position-effect variegation result from mutations in mus209, the drosophila gene encoding PCNA. EMBO J. 13, 1450–1459 (1994).

Henglein, B., Chenivesse, X., Wang, J., Eick, D., Brechot, C.: Structure and cell cycle-regulated transcription of the human cyclin A gene. Proc. Natl. Acad. Sci. USA 91, 5490–5494 (1994).

Hengst, L., Dulic, V., Slingerland, J.M., Lees, E., Reed, S.I.: A cell cycle-regulated inhibitor of cyclin-dependent kinases. Proc. Natl. Acad. Sci. USA 91, 5291–5295 (1994).

Henk, J.M.: Classification and staging. In: Henk, J.M., Langdon, J.D. (eds.): Malignant tumors of the oral cavity. Edward Arnold London 1985, pp 71–79.

Hensel, C.H., Hsieh, C.-L., Gazdar, A.F., Johnson, B.E., Sakaguchi, A.Y., Naylor, S.L., Lee, W.-H., Lee, E.Y.-H.: Altered structure and expression of the human retinoblastoma susceptibility gene in small cell lung cancer. Cancer Res. 50, 3067–3072 (1990).

Herrlich, P., Rahmsdorf, H.J.: Transcriptional and post-transcriptional responses to DNA-damaging agents. Curr. Opin. Cell Biol. 6, 425–431 (1994).

Herrmann, D.: Karzinomentstehung bei oralem Lichen planus. Langzeituntersuchung an 919 Patienten. Dtsch. Zahnärztl. Z. 47, 877–879 (1992). (English abstract)

Hinds, P.W., Dowdy, S.F., Eaton, E.N., Arnold, A., Weinberg, R.A.: Function of a human cyclin gene as an oncogene. Proc. Natl. Acad. Sci. USA 91, 709–713 (1994).

Hinds, P.W., Mittnacht, S., Dulic, V., Arnold, A., Reed, S.I., Weinberg, R.A.: Regulation of retinoblastoma protein functions by ectopic expression of human cyclins. Cell 70, 993–1006 (1992).

Hinds, P.W., Weinberg, R.A.: Tumor suppressor genes. Curr. Opin. Genet. Dev. 4, 135–141 (1994).

Hirota, J., Yoneda, K., Osaki, T.: Destruction of basement membrane and cell infiltrates in oral lichen planus. Path. Res. Pract. 185, 218–224 (1989).

Hitchcock, C.L.: Ki-67 staining as a means to simplify analysis of tumor cell proliferation. Am. J. Clin. Pathol. 96, 444–446 (1991).

Hogewind, W.F., van der Kwast, W.A., van der Waal, I.: Oral leukoplakia with emphasis on malignant transformation. J. Cranio-Max.-Fac. Surg. 17, 128–133 (1989).

Hollingsworth, R.E. Jr., Hensey, C.E., Lee, W.-H.: Retinoblastoma protein and the cell cycle. Curr. Opin. Genet. Dev. 3, 55–62 (1993).

Hollstein, M., Marion, M.-J., Lehman, T., Welsh, J., Harris, C.C., Martel-Planche, G., Kusters, I., Montesano, R.: p53 mutations at A:T base pairs in angiosarcomas of vinyl chloride-exposed factory workers. Carcinogenesis 15, 1–3 (1994b).

Hollstein, M., Rice, K., Greenblatt, M.S., Soussi, T., Fuchs, R., Sorlie, T., Hovig, E., Smith-Sorensen, B., Montesano, R., Harris, C.C.: Database of p53 gene somatic muations in human tumors and cell lines. Nucl. Acid. Res. 22, 3551–3555 (1994a).

Hollstein, M., Sidransky, D., Vogelstein, B., Harris, C.C.: p53 mutations in human cancers. Science 253, 49–53 (1991).

Holmstrup, P., Thorn, J. J., Rindum J., Pindborg, J.J.: Malignant development of lichen planus-affected oral mucosa. J. Oral Pathol. 17, 219–225 (1988).

Holmstrup, P.: The controversy of a premalignant potential of oral lichen planus is over. Oral Surg. Oral Med. Oral Pathol. 73, 704–706 (1992).

Homann, N., Andl, T., Nees, M., Schuhmann, A., Herold-Mende, C., Bosch, F.X.: Die Bedeutung von aberrantem p53-Protein in Kopf-Hals-Tumoren und sein Einfluss auf Proliferation und Differenzierung. HNO 41, 254–260 (1993).

Hong, W.K., Bromer, R.H., Amato, D.A., Shapshay, S., Vincent, M., Vaughan, C., Willett, B., Katz, A., Welch, J., Fofonoff, S., Strong, M.S.: Patterns of relapse in locally advanced head and neck cancer patients who achieved complete remission after combined modality therapy. Cancer 56, 1242– 1245 (1985).

Hong, W.K., Endicott, J., Itri, L., Doos, W., Batsakis, J.G., Bell, R., Fofonoff, S., Byers, R., Atkinson, N.E., Vaughan, S., Toth, B.B., Kramer, A., Dimery, I.W., Skipper, P., Strong, S.: 13-cis-retinoic acid in the treatment of oral leukoplakia. N. Engl. J. Med. 315, 1501–1505 (1986).

Hornstein, O. P., Schirner, E., Schell, H.: Prädilektionsstellen von Leukoplakien und Karzinomen der Mundschleimhaut. Dtsch. med. Wschr. 106, 1168–1173 (1981). (english abstract)

Horowitz, J.M., Yandell, D.W., Park, S.-H., Canning, S., Whyte, P., Buchkovich, K., Harlow, E., Weinberg, R.A., Dryja, T.P.: Point mutational inactivation of the retinoblastoma antioncogene. Science 243, 937– 940 (1989).

Horowitz, J.M., Park, S.-H., Bogenmann, E., Cheng, J.-C., Yandell, D.W., Kaye, F.J., Minna, J.D., Dryja, T.P., Weinberg, R.A.: Frequent inactivation of the retinoblastoma anti-oncogene is restricted to a subset of human tumor cells. Proc. Natl. Acad. Sci. USA 87, 2775–2779 (1990).

Howaldt, H.-P., Frenz, M., Platz, H.: Proposal for a modified T-classification for oral cancer. J. Cranio-Maxillo-Facial Surg. 21, 96–101 (1992).

Hu, Q., Dyson, N., Harlow, E.: The regions of the retinoblastoma protein needed for binding to adenovirus E1A or SV40 large T antigen are common sites for mutations. EMBO J. 9, 1147–1155 (1990).

Huang, H.-J. S., Yee, J.-K., Shew, J.-Y., Chen, P.-L., Bookstein, R., Friedmann, T., Lee, E.Y.-H., Lee, W.-H.: Suppression of the neoplastic phenotype by replacement of the RB gene in human cancer cells. Science 242, 1563–1566 (1988).

Huber, M.H., Hong, W.K.: Biology and chemoprevention of head and neck cancer. Curr. Probl. Cancer 18, 85–140 (1994).

Hülsken, J., Behrens, J., Birchmeier, W.: Tumor-suppressor gene products in cell contacts: The cadherin-APC-armadillo connection. Curr. Opin. Cell Biol. 6, 711–716 (1994).

Hunter, T., Pines, J.: Cyclins and cancer II: Cyclin D and CDK inhibitors come of age. Cell 79, 573–582 (1994).

Issing, W.J., Wustrow, T.P., Heppt, W.J.: Oncogenes related to head and neck cancer. Anticancer Res. 13, 2541–2551 (1993).

Jacks, T., Fazeli, A., Schmitt, E.M., Bronson, R.T., Goodell, M.A., Weinberg, R.A.: Effects of an Rb mutation in the mouse. Nature 359, 295–300 (1992).

Jares, P., Fernández, P.L., Campo, E., Nadal, A., Bosch, F., Aiza, G., Nayach, I., Traserra, J., Cardesa, A.: PRAD-1 / cyclin D1 gene amplification correlates with messenger RNA overexpression and tumor progression in human laryngeal carcinomas. Cancer Res. 54, 4813–4817 (1994).

Jaskulski, D., de Riel, J.K., Mercer, W.E., Calabretta, B. Baserga, R.: Inhibiton of cellular proliferation by antisense oligodeoxynucleotides to PCNA Cyclin. Science 240, 1544–1546 (1988).

Jetten, A.M.: Multistep process of squamous differentiation in tracheobronchial epithelial cells in vitro: Analogy with epidermal differentiation. Env. Health Perspect. 80, 149–160 (1989).

Jiang, W., Zhang, Y.J., Kahn, S.M., Hollstein, M.C., Santella, R.M., Lu, S.H., Harris, C.C., Montesano, R., Weinstein, I.B.: Altered expression of the cyclin D1 and retinoblastoma genes in human esophageal cancer. Proc. Natl. Acad. Sci. USA 90, 9026–9030 (1993).

Jin, Y., Mertens, F.: Chromosome abnormalities in oral squamous cell carcinomas. Eur. J. Cancer Oral Oncol. 29B, 257–263 (1993).

Johnson, D.G., Schwarz, J.K., Cress, W.D., Nevins, J.R.: Expression of transcription factor E2F1 induces quiescent cells to enter S phase. Nature 365, 349–352 (1993).

Jolly, M.: Premalignant lesions of the oral mucosa. Aust. Dent. J. 21, 414–422 (1976).

Jones, A.S.: Prognosis in mouth cancer: Tumour factors. Eur. J. Cancer Oral Oncol. 30B, 8–15 (1994).

Jontell, M., Watts, S., Wallström, M., Levin, L., Sloberg, K.: Human papilloma virus in erosive oral lichen planus. J. Oral Pathol. Med. 19, 273–277 (1990).

Jovanovic, A., Schulten, E.A., Kostense, P.J., Snow, G.B., van der Waal, I.: Squamous cell carcinoma of the lip and oral cavity in The Netherlands; an epidemiological study of 740 patients. J. Cranio-Maxillo-Facial Surg. 21, 149–152 (1993).

Jung, M., Notario, V., Dritschilo, A.: Mutations of the p53 gene in radiation-sensitive and -resistent human squamous carcinoma cells. Cancer Res. 52, 6390–6393 (1992).

Juven, T., Barak, Y., Zauberman, A., George, D.L., Oren, M.: Wild type p53 can mediate sequence-specific transactivation of an internal promoter within the mdm2 gene. Oncogene 8, 3411–3416 (1993).

Kaelin, W.G., Ewen, M.E., Livingston, D.M.: Definition of the minimal simian virus 40 large T antigen- and adenovirus E1A-binding domain in the retinoblastoma gene product. Mol. Cell. Biol. 10, 3761–3769 (1990).

Kahn, M.A., Dockter, M.E., Herman-Petris, J.M.: Flow cytometric analysis of oral premalignant lesions: A pilot study and review. J. Oral Pathol. Med. 21, 1–6 (1992).

Kandioler, D., Foedinger, M., Mueller, M.R., Eckersberger, F., Mannhalter, C., Wolner, E.: Carcinogen-specific mutations in the p53 tumor suppressor gene in lung cancer. J. Thorac. Cardiovasc. Surg. 107, 1095–1098 (1994).

Kannan, S., Balaram, P., Radhakrishna Pillai, M., Jagadeesh Chandran, G., Krishnan Nair, M., Kartha, C.C., Augustine, J., Sudha, L., Mangalam, M.K.: Ultrastructural variations and assessment of malignant transformation risk in oral leukoplakia. Path. Res. Pract. 189, 1169–1180 (1993).

Kastan, M.B., Onyekwere, O., Sidransky, D., Vogelstein, B., Craig, R.W.: Participation of p53 protein in the cellular response to DNA damage. Cancer Res. 51, 6304–6311 (1991).

Kastan, M.B., Zhan, Q., El-Deiry, W.S., Carrier, F., Jacks, T., Walsh, W.V., Plunkett, B.S., Vogelstein, B., Fornace, A.J. Jr.: A mammalian cell cycle checkpoint pathway utilizing p53 and GADD45 is defective in ataxia-telangiectasia. Cell 71, 587–597 (1992).

Kato, J.-Y., Matsuoka, M., Polyak, K., Massagué, J., Sherr, C.J.: Cyclic AMP-induced G1 phase arrest mediated by an inhibitor (p27^{Kip1}) of cyclin-dependent kinase 4 activation. Cell 79, 487–496 (1994).

Kato, J.-Y., Sherr, C.J.: Inhibition of granulocyte differentiation by G1 cyclins D2 and D3 but not D1. Proc. Natl. Acad. Sci. USA 90, 11513–11517 (1993).

Katz, R.W., Brahim, J.S., Travis, W.D.: Oral squamous cell carcinoma arising in a patient with long-standing lichen planus. Oral Surg. Oral Med. Oral Pathol. 70, 282–285 (1990).

Kaur, J., Srivastava, A., Ralhan, R.: Overexpression of p53 protein in betel- and tobacco-related human oral dysplasia and squamous-cell carcinoma in India. Int. J. Cancer 58, 340–345 (1994).

Kaye, F.J., Kratzke, R.A., Gerster, J.L., Horowitz, M.: A single amino acid substitution results in a retinoblastoma protein defective in phosphorylation and oncoprotein binding. Proc. Natl. Acad. Sci. USA 87, 6922–6926 (1990).

Keller, A.Z.: Cirrhosis of the liver, alcoholism and heavy smoking associated with cancer of the mouth and pharynx. Cancer 20, 1015–1022 (1967).

Kern, S.E., Kinzler, K.W., Bruskin, A., Jarosz, D., Friedman, P., Prives, C., Vogelstein, B.: Identification of p53 as a sequence-specific DNA-binding protein. Science 252, 1708–1711 (1991).

Kern, S.E., Pietenpol, J.A., Thiagalingam, S., Seymour, A., Kinzler, K.W., Vogelstein, B.: Oncogenic forms of p53 inhibit p53-regulated gene expression. Science 256, 827–830 (1992).

Ketcham, A.S., Wexler, H., Mantel, N.: Effects of alcohol in mouse neoplasia. Cancer Res. 23, 667–670 (1963).

Key, G., Meggetto, F., Becker, M.H., al-Saati, T., Schlüter, C., Duchrow, M., Deleol, G., Gerdes, J.: Immunohistochemical characterization of the antigen detected by monoclonal antibody IND.64. Evidence that IND.64 reacts with the cell proliferation associated nuclear antigen previously defined by Ki-67. Virchows Arch. B Cell Pathol. Incl. Mol. Pathol. 4, 259–262 (1992).

Keyomarsi, K., O'Leary, N., Molnar, G., Less, E., Fingert, H.J., Pardee, A.B.: Cyclin E, a potential prognostic marker for breast cancer. Cancer Res. 54, 380–385 (1994).

Keyomarsi, K., Pardee, A.B.: Redundant cyclin overexpression and gene amplification in breast cancer cells. Proc. Natl. Acad. Sci. USA 90, 1112–1116 (1993).

Khanna, J.M., Israel, Y.: Ethanol metabolism. In: Javitt, N.B. (ed.): Liver and biliary tract physiology I. University Park Press Baltimore 1980, pp 275–315.

Khatib, Z.A., Matsushime, H., Valentine, M., Shapiro, D.N., Sherr, C.J., Look, A.T.: Coamplification of the CDK4 gene with MDM2 and GLI in human sarcomas. Cancer Res. 53, 5535–5541 (1993).

Khorana, S., Gagel, F., Cote, G.J.: Direct sequencing of PCR products in agarose gel slices. Nucl. Acid Res. 22, 3425–3426 (1994).

Kim, M.S., Li, S.-L., Bertolami, C.N., Cherrick, H.M., Park, N.-H.: State of p53, Rb and DCC tumor suppressor genes in human oral cancer cell lines. Anticancer Res 13, 1405–1413 (1993).

Kiyokawa, H., Richon, V.M., Rifkind, R.A., Marks, P.A.: Suppression of cyclin-dependent kinase 4 during induced differentiation of erythroleukemia cells. Mol. Cell. Biol. 14, 7195–7203 (1994).

Kleinman, D.V., Swango, P.A., Pindborg, J.J., Gupta, P.: Toward assessing trends in oral mucosal lesions: Lessons learned from oral cancer. Adv. Dent. Res. 7, 32–41 (1993).

Knudsen, A.G. Jr.: Mutation and cancer: Statistical study of retinoblastoma. Proc. Natl. Acad. Sci. USA 68, 820–823 (1971).

Koch, H.: Karzinome der Mundhöhle. Forsch.-Berichte Nordrhein-Westfalen, Nr. 2421. Westdeutscher Verlag Opladen 1974.

Koch, W.M., Boyle, J.O., Mao, L., Hakim, J., Hruban, R.H., Sidransky, D.: p53 gene mutations as markers of tumor spread in synchronous oral cancers. Arch. Otolaryngol. Head Neck Surg. 120, 943–947 (1994).

Koff, A., Cross, F., Fisher, A., Schuhmacher, J., Leguellec, K., Philippe, M., Roberts, J.M.: Human cyclin E, a new cyclin that interacts with two members of the CDC2 gene family. Cell 66, 1217–1228 (1991).

Koff, A., Ohtsuki, M., Polyak, K., Roberts, J.M., Massague, J.: Negative regulation of G1 in mammalian cells: Inhibition of cyclin E-dependent kinase by TGF-beta. Science 260, 536–539 (1993).

Kohn, K.W., Jackman, J., O'Connor, P.M.: Cell cycle control and cancer chemotherapy. J. Cell. Biochem. 54, 440–452 (1994).

Kokal, W.A., Gardner, R.L., Sheibani, K., Zak, I.W., Beatty, J.D., Riihimaki, D.U., Wagman, L.D., Terz, J.J.: Tumor DNA content as a prognostic indicator in squamous cell carcinoma of the head and neck region. Am. J. Surg. 156, 276–280 (1988).

Kovar, H., Auinger, A., Jug, G., Aryee, D., Zoubek, A., Salzer-Kuntschik, M., Gadner, H.: Narrow spectrum of infrequent p53 mutations and absence of MDM2 amplification in Ewing tumors. Oncogene 8, 2683–2690 (1993).

Kövesi, G., Bánóczy, J.: Follow-up studies in oral lichen planus. Int. J. Oral Surg. 2, 13–19 (1973).

Krek, W., Ewen, M.E., Shirodkar, S., Arany, Z., Kaelin, W.G. Jr., Livingston, D.M.: Negative regulation of the growth-promoting transcription factor E2F-1 by a stably bound cyclin A-dependent protein kinase. Cell 78, 161–172 (1994).

Krutchkoff, D.J., Cutler, L., Laskowski, S.: Oral lichen planus: The evidence regarding potential malignant transformation. J. Oral Pathol. 7, 1–7 (1978).

Kuerbitz, S.J., Plunkett, B.S., Walsh, W.V. Kastan, M.B.: Wild-type p53 is a cell cycle checkpoint determinant following irradiation. Proc. Natl. Acad. Sci. USA 89, 7491–7495 (1992).

Kupryjanczyk, J., Thor, A.D., Beauchamp, R., Merritt, V., Edgerton, S.M., Bell, D.A., Yandell, D.W.: p53 gene mutation and protein accumulation in human ovarian cancer. Prod. Natl. Acad. Sci. USA 90, 7262–7266 (1993).

Kurihara, K., Hashimoto, N.: The pathological significance of Langerhans cells in oral cancer. J. Oral Pathol. 14, 289–298 (1985).

Kurki, P., Ogata, K., Tan, E.M.: Monoclonal antibodies to proliferating cell nuclear antigen (PCNA) / cyclin as probes for proliferating cells by immunofluorescence microscopy and flow cytometry. J. Immunol. Methods 109, 49–59 (1988).

Kurki, P., Vanderlaan, M., Dolbaere, F., Gray, J., Tan, E.M.: Expression of proliferating cell nuclear antigen (PCNA) / cyclin during the cell cycle. Exp. Cell Res. 166, 209–219 (1986).

Kurokawa, H., Tsuru, S., Okada, M., Nakamura, T., Kajiyama, M.: Evaluation of tumor markers in patients with squamous cell carcinoma in the oral cavity. Int. J. Oral Maxillofac. Surg. 22, 35–38 (1993).

Labrecque, S., Naor, N., Thomson, D., Matlashewski, G.: Analysis of the anti-p53 antibody response in cancer patients. Cancer Res. 53, 3468–3471 (1993).

Lacy, M.F., Reade, P.C., Hay, K.D.: Lichen planus: A theory of pathogenesis. Oral Surg. 56, 521–526 (1983).

Ladanyi, M., Cha, C., Lewis, R., Jhanwar, S.C., Huvos, A.G., Healey, J.H.: MDM2 gene amplification in metastatic osteosarcoma. Cancer Res. 53, 16–18 (1993).

Lammie, G.A., Fantl, V., Smith, R., Schuuring, E., Brookes, S., Michailides, R., Dickson, C.I., Arnold, A., Peters, G.: D11S218, a putative oncogene on chromosome 11q13 is amplified and expressed in squamous cell and mammary carcinomas and linked to BCL-1. Oncogene 6, 439–444 (1991).

Lane, D.P., Benchimol, S.: p53: Oncogene or antioncogene? Genes Dev. 4, 1–8 (1990).

Lane, D.P.: p53, guardian of the genome. Nature 358, 15–16 (1992).

Langdon, J.D., Partridge, M.: Expression of the tumour suppressor gene p53 in oral cancer. Br. J. Oral Maxillofac. Surg. 30, 214–220 (1992).

Langdon, J.D.: Epidemiology and aetiology. In: Henk, J.M., Langdon, J.D. (eds.): Malignant tumors of the oral cavity. Edward Arnold London 1985, pp 1–13.

Largey, J.S., Meltzer, S.J., Yin, J., Norris, K., Sauk, J.J., Archibald, D.W.: Loss of heterozygosity of p53 in oral cancers demonstrated by the polymerase chain reaction. Cancer 71, 1933–1937 (1993).

Laufer, J., Kuffer, R.: Le lichen plan buccal. Rev. Stomatol. (Paris) 72, 214–233, (1971).

Lay, K.M., Sein, K., Myint, A., Ko, S.K., Pindborg, J.J.: Epidemiologic study of 6000 villagers of oral precancerous lesions in Bilugyun: Preliminary report. Community Dent. Oral Epidemiol. 10, 152–155 (1982).

Leach, F.S., Tokino, T., Meltzer, P., Burrell, M., Oliner, J.D., Smith, S., Hill, D.E., Sidransky, D., Kinzler, K.W., Vogelstein, B.: p53 mutation and MDM2 amplification in human soft tissue sarcomas. Cancer Res. 53, 2231–2234 (1993).

Lee, E.Y.-H., Chang, C.-Y., Hu, N., Wang, Y.-C., Lai, C.-C., Herrup, K., Lee, W.-H., Bradley, A.: Mice deficient for Rb are nonviable and show defects in neurogenesis and haematopoiesis. Nature 359, 288–294 (1992).

Lee, E.Y.-H., To, H., Shew, J.-Y., Bookstein, R., Scully, P., Lee, W.-H.: Inactivation of the retinoblastoma susceptibility gene in human breast cancers. Science 241, 218–221 (1988).

Lee, J.S., Kim, S.Y., Hong, W.K., Lippman, S.M., Ro, J.Y., Gay, M.L., Hittelman, W.N.: Detection of chromosomal polysomy in oral leukoplakia, a premalignant lesion. J. Nat. Cancer Inst. 85, 1951–1954 (1993b).

Lee, N.K., Ye, Y.W., Chen, J., Li, X., Waber, P.G., Nisen, P.D.: p53, retinoblastoma, and human papillomavirus in squamous cell carcinoma and adjacent normal mucosa of the upper aerodigestive tract. Arch. Otolaryngol. Head Neck Surg. 119, 1125–1131 (1993a).

Lee, W.-H., Shew, J.-Y., Hong, F.D., Sery, T.W., Donoso, L.A., Young, L.-J., Bookstein, R., Lee, E.Y.-H.: The retinoblastoma susceptibility gene encodes a nuclear phosphoprotein associated with DNA binding activity. Nature 329, 642–645 (1987).

Lees, E., Faha, B., Dulic, V., Reed, S.I., Harlow, E.: Cyclin E / cdk2 and cyclin A / cdk2 kinases associate with p107 and E2F in a temporally distinct manner. Genes Dev. 6, 1874–1885 (1992).

Lennon, S.V., Martin, S.J., Cotter, T.G.: Dose-dependant induction of apoptosis in human tumour cell lines by widely diverging stimuli. Cell Prolif. 24, 203–214 (1991).

Lewensohn-Fuchs, I., Munck-Wikland, E., Berke, Z., Magnusson, K.P., Pallesen, G., Auer, G., Lindholm, J., Linde, A., Aberg, B., Rubio, C., Kuylenstierna, R., Wiman, K.G., Dalianis, T.: Involvement of aberrant p53 expression and human papillomavirus in carcinoma of the head, neck and esophagus. Anticancer Res. 14, 1281–1285 (1994).

Li, R., Waga, S., Hannon, G.J., Beach, D., Stillman, B.: Differential effects by the p21 CDK inhibitor on PCNA-dependent DNA replication and repair. Nature 371, 534–537 (1994b).

Li, Y., Jenkins, C.W., Nichols, M.A., Xiong, Y.: Cell cycle expression and p53 regulation of the cyclin-dependent kinase inhibitor p21. Oncogene 9, 2261–2268 (1994a).

Lickint, F.: Tabak und Tabakrauch als ätiologischer Faktor des Carcinoms. Z. Krebsforsch. 80, 349–365 (1930).

Lieber, C.S., Garro, A., Leo, M.A., Mak, K.M., Worner, T.: Alcohol and Cancer. Hepatology 6, 1005–1019 (1986).

Lind, P.O.: Malignant transformation in oral leukoplakia. Scand. J. Dent. Res. 95, 449–455 (1987).

Lind, P.O., Koppang, H.S., Aas, E.: Malignant transformation in oral lichen planus. Int. J. Oral Surg. 14, 509–516 (1985).

Lippman, S., Kessler, J., Meyskens, F.: Retinoids as preventive and therapeutic anticancer agents (Part 1). Cancer Treat Rep. 71, 391–405 (1987).

Lippman, S.M., Lee, J.S., Lotan, R., Hittelman, W., Wargovich, M.J., Hong, W.K.: Biomarkers as intermediate end points in chemoprevention trials. J. Natl. Cancer Inst. USA 82, 555–560 (1990).

Liu, T.J., Zhang, W.W., Taylor, D.L., Roth, J.A., Goepfert, H., Clayman, G.L.: Growth suppression of human head and neck cancer cells by the introduction of a wild-type p53 gene via a recombinant adenovirus. Cancer Res. 54, 3662–3667 (1994).

Livingstone, L. R., White, A., Sprouse, J., Livanos, E., Jacks, T., Tlsty, T.D.: Altered cell cycle arrest and gene amplification potential accompany loss of wild-type p53. Cell 70, 923–935 (1992).

Lombardi, T., Hauser, C., Budtz-Jörgensen, E.: Langerhans cells: Structure, function and role in oral pathological conditions. J. Oral Pathol. Med. 22, 193–202 (1993).

Lorz, M., Meyer-Breiting, E., Bettinger, R.: Proliferating cell nuclear antigen counts as markers of cell proliferation in head and neck cancer. Eur. Arch. Otorhinolaryngol. 251, 91–94 (1994).

Lotan, R.: Squamous cell differentiation markers in normal, premalignant, and malignant epithelium: Effects of retinoids. J. Cell. Biochem. Suppl. 17F, 167–174 (1993).

Lovec, H., Grzeschiczek, A., Kowalski, M.-B., Möröy, T.: Cyclin D1 / bcl-1 cooperates with myc gens in the generation of B-cell lymphoma in transgenic mice. EMBO J. 13, 3487–3495 (1994a).

Lovec, H., Sewing., A., Lucibello, F.C., Müller, R., Möröy, T.: Oncogenic activity of cyclin D1 revealed through cooperation with Ha-ras: Link between cell cycle control and malignant transformation. Oncogene 9, 323–326 (1994b).

Lowe, S.W., Ruley, H.E., Jacks, T., Housman, D.E.: p53-dependent apoptosis modulates the cytotoxicity of anticancer agents. Cell 74, 957–967 (1993a).

Lowe, S.W., Schmitt, E.M., Smith, S.W., Osborne, B.A., Jacks, T.: p53 is required for radiation-induced apoptosis in mouse thymocytes. Nature 362, 847–849 (1993b).

Lu, X., Lane, D.: Differential induction of transcriptionally active p53 following UV or ionizing radiation: Defects in chromosome instability syndromes? Cell 75, 765–778 (1993).

Ludlow, J. W., DeCaprio, J. A., Huang, C.-M., Lee, W.-H., Paucha, E., Livingston, D.M.: SV40 large T antigen binds preferentially to an underphosphorylated member of the retinoblastoma susceptibility gene product family. Cell 56, 57–65 (1989).

Ludlow, J. W., Shon, J., Pipas, J.M., Livingston, D.M., DeCaprio, J. A.: The retinoblastoma susceptibility gene product undergoes cell cycle-dependent dephosphorylation and binding to and release from SV40 large T. Cell 60, 387–396 (1990).

Lukas, J., Muller, H., Bartkova, J., Spitkovsky, D., Kjerulff, A.A., Jansen-Durr, P., Strauss, M., Bartek, J.: DNA tumor virus oncoproteins and retinoblastoma gene mutations share the ability to relieve the cell's requirement for cyclin D1 function in G1. J. Cell Biol. 125, 625–638 (1994a).

Lukas, J., Pagano, M., Staskova, Z., Draetta, G., Bartek, J.: Cyclin D1 protein oscillates and is essential for cell cycle progression in human tumour cell lines. Oncogene 9, 707–718 (1994b).

Lundberg, C., Skoog, L., Cavenee, W.K., Nordenskjöld, M.: Loss of heterozygosity in human ductal breast tumors indicates a recessive muation on chromosome 13. Proc. Natl. Acad. Sci. USA 84, 2372–2376 (1987).

MacGeoch, C., Kennedy, S., Spurr, N.K.: Strategies for amplification of human Tp53 gene sequences. Technique 3, 179–182 (1991).

Maestro, R., Gasparotto, D., Vukosavljevic, T., Barzan, L., Sulfaro, S., Boiocchi, M.: Three discrete regions of deletion at 3p in head and neck cancers. Cancer Res. 53, 5775–5779 (1993).

Maier, H., Dietz, A., Gewelke, U., Seitz, H.K., Heller, W.-D.: Tabak- und alkoholassoziiertes Krebsrisiko im Bereich des oberen Atmungs- und Verdauungstraktes. Laryngo-Rhino-Otol. 69, 505–511 (1990).

Maity, A., McKenna, W.G., Muschel, R.J.: The molecular basis for cell cycle delays following ionizing radiation: A review. Radiother. Oncol. 31, 1–13 (1994).

Mak, K.M., Leo, M.A., Lieber, C.S.: Effect of ethanol and vitamin A deficiency on epithelial cell proliferation and structure in the rat esophagus. Gastroenterology 93, 362–370 (1987).

Malaker, K., Anderson, B.J., Beecroft, W.A., Hodson, D.: Management of oral mucosal dysplasia with β-carotene retinoic acid: A pilot cross-over study. Cancer Detec. Prev. 15, 335–340 (1991).

Mao, L., Brennan, J.A., Hruban, R.H., Boyle, J.O., Eby, Y.J., Koch, W.M., Sidransky, D.: Molecular assessment of histopathologic staging. Head Neck 16, 502 (1994).

Mao, L., Sidransky, D.: Cancer screening based on genetic alterations in human tumors. Cancer Res. 54 (7 Suppl), 1939s–1940s (1994).

Marchetta, F.C., Sako, K., Camp, F.: Multiple malignancies in patients with head and neck cancer. Am. J. Surg. 110, 537–541 (1965).

Marshall, J.R., Graham, S., Haughey, B., Shedd, D., O'Shea, R., Brasure, J., Wilkinson, G.S., West, D.: Smoking, alcohol, dentition and diet in the epidemiology of oral cancer. Eur. J. Cancer Oral Oncol. 28B, 9–15 (1992).

Martinez, J., Georgoff, I., Martinez, J., Levine, A.J.: Cellular localization and cell cycle regulation by a temperature-sensitive p53 protein. Genes Dev. 5, 151–159 (1991).

Mashberg, A., Garfinkel, L., Harris, S.: Alcohol as a primary risk factor in oral squamous cell carcinoma. CA-A Cancer J. Clin. 31, 146–155 (1981).

Massa, M.C., Greaney, V., Kron, T., Armin, A.: Malignant transformation of oral lichen planus: A case report and review of the literature. Cutis 45, 45–47 (1990).

Matlashewski, G., Banks, L., Pim, D., Crawford, L.: Analysis of human p53 proteins and mRNA levels in normal and transformed cells. Eur. J. Biochem. 154, 665–672 (1986).

Matsuoka, S., Yamaguchi, M., Matsukage, A.: D-type cyclin-binding regions of proliferating cell nuclear antigen. J. Biol. Chem. 269, 11030–11036 (1994).

Matsushime, H., Roussel, M.F., Ashmun, R.A., Sherr, C.J.: Colony-stimulating factor 1 regulates novel cyclins during the G1 phase of the cell cycle. Cell 65, 701–713 (1991).

Matthews, J.B., Sully, C., Jovanovic, A., van der Waal, I., Yeudall, W.A., Prime, S.S.: Relationship of tobacco / alcohol use to p53 expression in patients with lingual squamous cell carcinomas. Eur. J. Cancer Oral Oncol. 29B, 285–289 (1993).

Mattijssen, V., Peters, H.M., Schalkwijk, L., Manni, J.J., van't Hof-Grootenboer, B., de Mulder, P.H., Ruiter, D.J.: E-cadherin expression in head and neck squamous-cell carcinoma is associated with clinical outcome. Int. J. Cancer 55, 580–585 (1993).

McCarthy, F.P.: Etiology, pathology and treatment of leukoplakia buccalis with a report of 316 cases. Arch. Dermatol. Syph. 34, 612–623 (1936).

McCarthy, P.L., Shklar, G.: Diseases of the oral mucosa. 2nd ed., Lea & Febiger Philadelphia 1980.

McDaniel, T., Carbone, D., Takahashi, T., Chumakov, P., Chang, E.H., Pirollo, K.F., Yin, J., Huang, Y., Meltzer, S.J.: The MspI polymorphism in intron 6 of p53 (TP53) detected by digestion of PCR products. Nucleic Acids Res. 19, 4796 (1991).

McGregor, G.I., Davis, N., Robins, R.E.: Squamous cell carcinoma of the tongue and lower oral cavity in patients under 40 years of age. Am. J. Surg. 146, 88–92 (1983).

McIlwrath, A.J., Vasey, P.A., Ross, G.M., Brown, R.: Cell cycle arrests and radiosensitivity of human tumor cell lines: Dependence on wild-type p53 for radiosensitivity. Cancer Res. 54, 3718–3722 (1994).

Mehta, F.S., Gupta, P.C., Pindborg, J.J.: Chewing and smoking habits in relation to precancer and oral cancer. J. Cancer Res. Clin. Oncol. 99, 35–39 (1981).

Mehta, F.S., Pindborg, J.J., Gupta, P.C., Daftary, D.K.: Epidemiologic and histologic study of oral cancer and leukoplakia among 50,915 villagers in india. Cancer 24, 832–849 (1969).

Mercer, W.E., Baserga, R.: Expression of p53 protein during the cell cycle of human peripheral blood lymphocytes. Genes Dev. 5, 151–159 (1991).

Michieli, P., Chedid, M., Lin, D., Pierce, J.H., Mercer, W.E., Givol, D.: Induction of WAF1 / CIP1 by a p53-independent pathway. Cancer Res. 54, 3391–3395 (1994).

Mietz, J.A., Unger, T., Huibregtse, J., Howley, P.M.: The transcriptional transactivation function of wild-type p53 is inhibited by SV 40 large T-antigen and by HPV-16 E6 protein. EMBO J. 11, 5013–5020 (1992).

Mihara, K., Cao, X.-R., Yen, A., Chandler, S., Driscoll, B., Murphree, A.L., T'Ang, A., Fung, Y.-K.: Cell cycle-dependent regulation of phosphorylation of the human retinoblastoma gene product. Science 246, 1300–1303 (1989).

Milde-Langosch, K., Löning, T., Meichsner, M., Henke, R.-P.: HPV-Infektionen in Tumoren des oberen Atmungs- und Verdauungstraktes. In-situ-Hybridisierung und Dot-blot-Hybridisierung mit biotinylierten DNA-Proben. Acta histochemica. Suppl. 37, 103–108 (1989).

Miller, C.S., Zeuss, M.S., White, D.K.: Detection of HPV DNA in oral carcinoma using polymerase chain reaction together with in situ hybridization. Oral Surg. Oral Med. Oral Pathol. 77, 480–486 (1994).

Moll, U.M., Riou, G., Levine, A.J.: Two distinct mechanisms alter p53 in breast cancer: Mutation and nuclear exclusion. Proc. Natl. Acad. Sci. 89, 7262–7266 (1992).

Momand, J., Zambetti, G.P., Olson, D.C., George, D., Levine, A.J.: The mdm-2 oncogene product forms a complex with the p53 protein and inhibits p53-mediated transactivation. Cell 69, 1237– 1245 (1992).

Moncarz, V., Ulmansky, M., Lustmann, J.: Lichen planus: Exploring its malignant potential. J. Am. Dent. Assoc. 124, 102–108 (1993).

Montgomery, D.S., Culver, G.D.: Lichen planus of the mouth alone. Br. J. Dermatol. 41, 45–50 (1929).

Morgenbessser, S.D., Williams, B.O., Jacks, T., DePinho, R.A.: p53-dependent apoptosis produced by Rb-deficiency in the developing mouse lens. Nature 371, 72–74 (1994).

Mori, N., Yokota, J., Akiyama, T., Sameshima, Y., Okamoto, A., Mizoguchi, H., Toyoshima, K., Sugimura, T., Terada, M.: Variable muations of the RB gene in small-cell lung carcinoma. Oncogene 5, 1713–1717 (1990).

Mori, T., Miura, K., Aoki, T., Nishihira, T., Mori, S., Nakamura, Y.: Frequent somatic mutation of the MTS1 / CDK4I (multiple tumor suppressor / cyclin-dependent kinase 4 inhibitor) gene in esophageal squamous cell carcinoma. Cancer Res. 54, 3396–3397 (1994).

Morris, G.F., Mathews, M.B.: Regulation of proliferating cell nuclear antigen during the cell cycle. J. Biol. Chem. 264, 13856–13864 (1989).

Motokura, T., Arnold, A.: Cyclin D and oncogenesis. Curr. Opin. Genet. Dev. 3, 5–10 (1993).

Motokura, T., Bloom, T., Kim, H.G., Jüppner, H., Ruderman, J.V., Kronenberg, H.M., Arnold, A.: A novel cyclin encoded by a bcl1-linked candidate oncogene. Nature 350, 512–515 (1991).

Muller, D., Millon, R., Lidereau, R., Engelmann, A., Bronner, G., Flesch, H., Eber, M., Methlin, G., Abecassis, J.: Frequent amplification of 11q13 DNA markers is associated with lymph node involvement in human head and neck squamous cell carcinomas. Eur. J. Cancer Oral Oncol. 30B, 113–120 (1994).

Müller, H., Lukas, J., Schneider, A., Warthoe, P., Bartek, J., Eilers, M., Strauss, M.: Cyclin D1 expression is regulated by the retinoblastoma protein. Proc. Natl. Acad. Sci. USA 91, 2945–2949 (1994).

Münger, K., Werness, B.A., Dyson, N., Phelps, W.C., Harlow, E., Howley, P.M.: Complex formation of human papillomavirus E7 proteins with the retinoblastoma tumor suppressor gene product. EMBO J. 8, 4099–4105 (1989).

Murray, A. W.: Cell cycle checkpoints. Curr. Opin. Cell Biol. 6, 872–876 (1994).

Murray, A., Hunt, T.: The cell cycle—an introduction. Oxford University Press New York 1993.

Murray, A.W.: Creative blocks: Cell cycle checkpoints and feedback controls. Nature 359, 599–604 (1992).

Murti, P.R., Daftary, D.K., Bhonsle, R.B., Gupta, P.C., Mehta, F.S., Pindborg, J.J.: Malignant potential of oral lichen planus: Observations in 722 patients from India. J. Oral Path. 15, 71–77 (1986).

Nakashima, T., Yano, G., Hayashi, I., Katsuta, Y.: Epithelial membrane antigen and S-100 protein-labeled cells in primary and metastatic laryngeal carcinomas. Head Neck 14, 445–451 (1992).

Nathanson, A., Agren, K., Biörklund, A., Lind, M.G., Andréason, L., Anniko, M., Freijd, A., Lejdeborn, L., Kinman, S., Kumlien, A., Köling, A., Lindström, J., Novik, A., Olofsson, J., Pettersson, K.-I.: Evaluation of some prognostic factors in squamous cell carcinoma of the mobile tongue: A multicenter study in Sweden. Head Neck 11, 387–392 (1989).

Nawroz, H., van der Riet, P., Hruban, R.H., Koch, W., Ruppert, J.M., Sidransky, D.: Allelotype of head and neck squamous cell carcinoma. Cancer Res. 54, 1152–1155 (1994).

Nees, M., Homann, N., Discher, H., Andl, T., Enders, C., Herold-Mende, C., Schuhmann, A., Bosch, F.X.: Expression of mutated p53 occurs in tumor-distant epithelia of head and neck cancer patients: A possible molecular basis for the development of multiple tumors. Cancer Res. 53, 4189–4196 (1993).

Neumann-Jensen, B., Holmstrup, P., Pindborg, J.J.: Smoking habits of 611 patients with oral lichen planus. Oral Surg. Oral Med. Oral Pathol. 43, 410–415 (1977).

Nevins, J.R.: Cell cycle targets of the DNA tumor viruses. Curr. Opin. Genet. Dev. 4, 130–134 (1994).

Nevins, J.R.: E2F: A link between the Rb tumor suppressor protein and viral oncoproteins. Science 258, 424–429 (1992).

Nigro, J.M., Baker, S.J., Preisinger, A.C., Jessup, J.M., Hostetter, R., Cleary, K., Bigner, S.H., Davidson, N., Baylin, S., Devilee, P., Glover, T., Collins, F.S., Weston, A., Modali, R., Harris, C.C., Vogelstein, B.: Mutations in the p53 gene occur in diverse human tumour types. Nature 342, 705–708 (1989).

Nishioka, H., Hiasa, Y., Hayashi, I., Kitahori, Y., Konishi, N., Sugimora, M.: Immunohistochemical detection of p53 oncoprotein in human oral squamous cell carcinomas and leukoplakias: Comparison with proliferating cell nuclear antigen staining and correlation with clinicopathological findings. Oncology 50, 426–429 (1993).

Nobori, T., Miura, K., Wu, D.J., Lois, A., Takabayashi, K., Carson, D.A.: Deletions of the cyclin-dependent kinase-4 inhibitor gene in multiple human cancers. Nature 368, 753–756 (1994).

Noda, A., Ning, Y., Venable, S.F., Pereira-Smith, O.M., Smith J.R.: Cloning of senescent cell-derived inhibitors of DNA synthesis using an expression screen. Exp. Cell Res. 211, 90–98 (1994).

Nylander, K., Anneroth, G., Gustafsson, H., Roos, G., Stenling, R., Zackrisson, B.: Cell kinetics of head and neck squamous cell carcinomas. Prognostic implications. Acta Oncol. 33, 23–28 (1994).

O'Connor, P.M., Kohn, K.W.: A fundamental role for cell cycle regulation in the chemosensitivity of cancer cells? Semin. Cancer Biol. 3, 409–416 (1992).

Ogawa, Y., Inomata, T., Nishioka, A., Maeda, T., Seguchi, H., Kishimoto, S., Saito, H., Hirota, J., Osaki, T.: Changes in the Ki-67 labeling rates of head and neck squamous cell carcinomas during preoperative radiation therapy. Oncology 49, 450–453 (1992).

Ogden, G.R., Kiddie, R.A., Lunny, D.P., Lane, D.P.: Assessment of p53 protein expression in normal, benign, and malignant oral mucosa. J. Path. 166, 389–394 (1992).

Ohtsubo, M., Roberts, J.M.: Cyclin-dependant regulation of G1 in mammalian fibroblasts. Science 259, 1908–1912 (1993).

Oliner, J.D., Kinzler, K.W., Meltzer, P.S., George, D.L., Vogelstein, B.: Amplification of a gene encoding a p53-associated protein in human sarcomas. Nature 358, 80–83 (1992).

Olson, D.C., Marechal, V., Momand, J., Chen, J., Romocki, S., Levine, A.J.: Identification and characterization of multiple mdm-2 proteins and mdm-2-p53 protein complexes. Onogene 8, 2353–2360 (1993).

Onadim, Z., Hogg, A., Baird, P.N., Cowell, J.K.: Oncogenic point mutation in exon 20 of the RB1 gene in families showing incomplete penetrance and mild expression of the retinoblastoma phenotype. Proc. Natl. Acad. Sci. USA 89, 6177–6181 (1992).

Oren, M., Reich, N.C., Levine, A.J.: Regulation of the cellular p53 tumor antigen in teratocarcinoma cells and their differentiated progeny. Mol. Cell. Biol. 2, 443–449 (1982).

Oren, M.: p53: The ultimate tumor suppressor gene. Faseb J. 6, 3169–3175 (1992).

Ouhayoun, J.-P., Gosselin, F., Forest, N., Winter, S., Franke, W.W.: Cytokeratin patterns in human oral epithelia: Differences in cytokeratin synthesis in gingival epithelium and the adjacent alveolar mucosa. Differentiation 30, 123–129 (1985).

Owens, W., Field, J.K., Howard, P.J., Stell, P.M.: Multiple cytogenetic aberrations in squamous cell carcinomas of the head and neck. Eur. J. Cancer Oral Oncol. 28B, 17–21 (1992).

Pan, H., Griep, A.E.: Altered cell cycle regulation in the lens of HPV-16 E6 or E7 transgenic mice: Implications tor tumor suppressor gene function in development. Genes Dev. 8, 1285–1299 (1994).

Pardee, A.B., Keyomarsi, K.: Modification of cell proliferation with inhibitors. Curr. Opin. Cell Biol. 4, 186–191 (1992).

Park, N.H., Li, S.-L., Xie, J.-F., Cherrick, H.M.: In vitro and animal studies of the role of viruses in oral carcinogenesis. Eur. J. Cancer Oral. Oncol. 28B, 145–152 (1992).

Parker, R.G., Enstrom, J.E.: Second primary cancers of the head and neck following treatment of initial primary head and neck cancers. Int. J. Radiat. Oncol. Biol. Phys. 14, 561–564 (1988).

Partridge, M., Kiguwa, S., Langdon, J.D.: Frequent deletion of chromosome 3p in oral squamous cell carcinoma. Eur. J. Cancer Oral Oncol. 30B, 248–251 (1994).

Paterlini, P., Suberville, A.M., Zindy, F., Melle, J., Sonnier, M., Marie, J.P., Dreyfus, F., Brechot, C.: Cyclin A expression in human hematological malignancies: A new marker of cell proliferation. Cancer Res. 53, 235–238 (1993).

Pavelic, Z.P., Gluckman, J.L., Gapany, M., Reising, J., Craven, J.M., Kelley, D.J., Pavelic, L., Gapany, S., Biddinger, P., Stambrook, P.J.: Improved immunohistochemical detection of p53 protein in paraffin-embedded tissues reveals elevated levels in most head and neck and lung carcinomas: Correlation with clinicopathological parameters. Anticancer Res. 12, 1389–1394 (1992).

Pavelic, Z.P., Li, Y.-Q., Stambrook, P.J., McDonald, J.S., Munck-Wikland, E., Pavelic, K., Dacic, S., Danilovic, Z., Pavelic, L., Mugge, R.E., Wilson, K., Nguyen, C., Gluckman, J.L.: Overexpression of p53 protein is common in premalignant head and neck cancer lesions. Anticancer Res. 14, 2259–2266 (1994).

Perry, M.E., Levine, A.J.: Tumor-suppressor p53 and the cell cycle. Curr. Opin. Gen. Dev. 3, 50–54 (1993).

Perry, M.E., Piette, J., Zawadzki, J.A., Harvey, D., Levine, A.J.: The mdm-2 gene is induced in response to UV light in a p53-dependent manner. Proc. Natl. Acad. Sci. 90, 11623–11627 (1993).

Peto, R., Doll, R., Buckley, J.D., Sporn, M.B.: Can dietary beta-carotene materially reduce human cancer rates? Nature 290, 201–208 (1981).

Picksley, S.M., Lane, D. P.: p53 and Rb: Their cellular roles. Curr. Opin. Cell Biol. 6, 853–858 (1994).

Picksley, S.M., Lane, D.P.: The p53-mdm2 autoregulatory feedback loop: A paradigm for the regulation of growth control by p53? BioEssays 15, 689–690 (1993).

Pietenpol, J.A., Tokino, T., Thiagalingam, S., El-Deiry, W.S., Kinzler, K.W., Vogelstein, B.: Sequence-specific transcriptional activation is essential for growth suppression by p53. Proc. Natl. Acad. Sci. 91, 1998–2002 (1994).

Pikkarainen, P.H., Salaspuro, M.P., Lieber, C.S.: A metohd for the determination of "free" acetaldehyde in plasma. Alcoholism: Clin. Exp. Res. 3, 259–261 (1979).

Pindborg, J.J., Bhatt, M., Devanath, K.R., Narayana, H.R., Ramachandra, S.: Frequency of oral white lesions among 10, 000 individuals in Bangalore, South India. Indian J. Med. Sci. 20, 349–352 (1966).

Pindborg, J.J., Chawla, T.N., Misra, R.K., Nagpaul, R.K., Gupta, V.K.: Frequency of oral carcinoma, leukoplakia, leukokeratosis, leukodema, submucous fibrosis, and lichen planus in 10,000 Indians in Lucknow, Uttar Pradesh, India. J. Dent. Res. 44, 615–618 (1965a).

Pindborg, J.J., Kalapessi, H.K., Kale, S.A., Singh, H., Talyarkhan, B.N.: Frequency of oral leukoplakias and related conditions among 10,000 Bombayites. J. All. India Dent. Ass. 37, 1–2 (1965).

Pindborg, J.J., Mehta, F.S., Daftary, D.K, Gupta, P.C., Bhonsle, R.B.: Prevalence of oral lichen planus among 7639 Indian villagers in Kerala, South India. Acta Dermatovener. (Stockholm) 52, 216–220 (1972).

Pindborg, J.J.: Atlas of diseases of the oral mucosa. 3rd ed., W.B. Saunders Philadelphia 1980.

Pindborg, J.J.: Clinical relevance of precancerous lesions of oral mucosa. Recent Results Cancer Res. 134, 9–16 (1994).

Pindborg, J.J.: Oral Cancer and Precancer. Wright, Bristol 1980.

Platz, H., Fries, R., Hudec, M.: Computer-aided individual prognoses of squamous cell carcinomas of the lips, oral cavity and oropharynx. Int. J. Oral Maxillofac. Surg. 21, 150–155 (1992).

Platz, H., Fries, R., Hudec, M.: Einführung in die "prospektive DÖSAK-Studie über Plattenepithelkarzinome der Lippen, der Mundhöhle und des Oropharynx". Dtsch. Z. Mund Kiefer GesichtsChir. 12, 293–302 (1988).

Platz, H., Fries, R., Hudec, M.: Prognosis of oral cavity carcinomas. Results of a multicentric retrospective observational study. Carl Hanser München 1986.

Pogrel, M.A., Weldon, L.L.: Carcinoma arising in erosive lichen planus in the midline of the dorsum of the tongue. Oral Surg. Oral Med. Oral Pathol. 55, 62–66 (1983).

Polyak, K., Kato, J.Y., Solomon, M.J., Sherr, C.J., Massague, J., Roberts, J.M., Koff, A.: p27Kip1, a cyclin-Cdk inhibitor, links transforming growth factor-beta and contact inhibition to cell cycle arrest. Genes Dev. 8, 9–22 (1994a).

Polyak, K., Lee, M.H., Erdjument-Bromage, H., Koff, A., Roberts, J.M., Tempst, P., Massague, J.: Cloning of p27Kip1, a cyclin-dependent kinase inhibitor and a potential mediator of extracellular antimitogenic signals. Cell 78, 59–66 (1994b).

Porter, K., Klouda, P., Scully, C., Bidwell, J., Porter, S.: Class I and II HLA antigens in British patients with oral lichen planus. Oral Surg. Oral Med. Oral Path. 75, 176–180 (1993).

Preudhomme, C., Quesnel, B., Vachee, A., Lepelley, P., Collyn-D'Hooghe, M., Wattel, E., Fenaux, P.: Absence of amplification of mdm2 gene, a regulator of p53 function, in myelodysplastic syndromes. Leukemia 7, 1291–1293 (1993).

Price, B.D., Park, S.J.: DNA damage increases the levels of mdm2 messenger RNA in wtp53 human cells. Cancer Res. 54, 896–899 (1994).

Puisieux, A., Lim, S., Groopman, J., Ozturk, M.: Selective targeting of p53 gene mutational hotspots in human cancers by etiologically defined carcinogenes. Cancer Res. 51, 6185–6189 (1991).

Ranasinghe, A., MacGeoch, C., Dyer, S., Spurr, N., Johnson, N.W.: Some oral carcinomas from Sri Lankan betel / tobacco chewers overexpress p53 oncoprotein but lack mutations in exons 5–9. Anticancer Res. 13, 2065–2068 (1993a).

Ranasinghe, A.W., Warnakulasuriya, K.A., Johnson, N.W.: Low prevalence of expression of p53 oncoprotein in oral carcinomas from Sri Lanka associated with betel and tobacco chewing. Eur. J. Cancer Oral Oncol. 29B, 147–150 (1993b).

Rassekh, C.H., Johnson, J.T., Eibling, D.E.: Circulating markers in squamous cell carcinoma of the head and neck: A review. Eur. J. Cancer Oral Oncol. 30B, 23–28 (1994).

Reddy, G.P.: Cell cycle: Regulatory events in G1-S transition of mammalian cells. J. Cell. Biochem. 54, 379–386 (1994).

Regezi, J.A., Sciubba, J.J.: Oral pathology. W.B. Saunders Philadelphia / London / Toronto / Montreal / Sydney / Tokyo 1989.

Regezi, J.A., Stewart, J.C.B., Lloyd, R.V., Headington, J.T.: Immunohistochemical staining of Langerhans' cells and macrophages in lichen planus. Oral Surg. Oral Med. Oral Pathol. 60, 396–402 (1985).

Reich, N.C., Levine, A.J.: Growth regulation of a cellular tumor antigen, p53 in nontransformed cells. Nature 308, 199–201 (1984).

Reichart, P.A., Mohr, U., Srisuwan, S., Geerlings, H., Theetranont, C., Kangwanpong, T.: Precancerous and other mucosal lesions related to chewing, smoking and drinking habits in Thailand. Community Dent. Oral Epidemiol. 15, 152–160 (1987).

Reid, B.J., Blount, P.L., Rubin, C.E., Levine, D.S., Haggitt, R.C., Rabinovitch, P.S.: Flow-cytometric and histological progression to malignancy in Barrett's esophagus: Prospective endoscopic surveillance of a cohort. Gastroenterology 102, 1212–1219 (1992).

Reifenberger, G., Liu, L., Ichimura, K., Schmidt, E. E., Collins, V.P.: Amplification and overexpression of the MDM2 gene in a subset of human malignant gliomas without p53 mutations. Cancer Res. 53, 2736–2739 (1993).

Reisman, R.J., Schwartz, A.E., Friedman, E.W., Gerry, R.G.: The malignant potential of oral lichen planus—diagnostic pitfalls. Oral Surg. Oral Med. Oral Pathol. 38, 227–232 (1974).

Renstrup, G., Pindborg, J.J.: Oral manifestations of lichen ruber. Ugeskr. Laeger <u>120</u>, 1327–1330 (1958).

Rheinwald, J.G., Beckett, M.A.: Defective terminal differentiation in culture as a consistent and selectable character of malignant human keratinocytes. Cell <u>22</u>, 629–632 (1980).

Rijzewijk, J.J., van Erp, P.E., Bauer F.W.: Two binding sites for Ki67 related to quiescent and cycling cells in human epidermis. Acta Derm. Venerol. (Stockholm) <u>69</u>, 512–515 (1989).

Rodrigues, N.R., Rowan, A., Smith, M.E., Kerr, I.B., Bodmer, W.F., Gannon, J.V., Lane, D.P.: p53 mutations in colon cancer. Proc. Natl. Acad. Sci. USA <u>87</u>, 7555–7559 (1990).

Rogel, A., Popliker, M., Webb, C.G., Oren, M.: P53 cellular tumor antigen: Analysis of mRNA levels in normal adult tissue, embryos and tumors. Mol. Cell. Biol. <u>5</u>, 2851–2855 (1985).

Rohde, B.: Zur Häufigkeit des Carcinoms der Mundschleimhaut und des Lippenrots auf dem Boden eines Lichen ruber. Arch. Klin. Exp. Dermatol. <u>227</u>, 815–818 (1966).

Roland, N.J., Caslin, A.W., Bowie, G.L., Jones, A.S.: Has the cellular proliferation marker Ki67 any clinical relevance in squamous cell carcinoma of the head and neck? Clin. Otolaryngol. <u>19</u>, 13–18 (1994).

Rosenberg, C.L., Motokura, T., Kronenberg, H.M., Arnold, A.: Coding sequence of the overexpressed transcript of the putative oncogene PRAD1 / cyclin D1 in two primary human tumors. Oncogene <u>8</u>, 519–521 (1993).

Ross, N.M., Gross, E.: Oral findings based on an automated multiphasic health screening program. J. Oral Med. <u>26</u>, 21–26 (1971).

Rothman, K., Keller, A.: The effect of joint exposure to alcohol and tobacco on risk of cancer of the mouth and pharynx. J. Chron. Dis. <u>25</u>, 711–716 (1972).

Rubio, M.-P., von Deimling, A., Yandell, D.W., Wiestler, O.D., Gusella, J.F., Louis, D.N.: Accumulation of wild type p53 protein in human astrocytomas. Cancer Res. <u>53</u>, 3465–3467 (1993).

Saiki, R.K., Gelfand, D.H., Stoffel, S., Scharf, S.J., Higuchi, R., Horn, G.T., Mullis, K.B., Erlich, H.A.: Primer-directed enzymatic amplification of DNA with a thermostable DNA polymerase. Science <u>239</u>, 487–491 (1988).

Sakai, E., Rikimaru, K., Ueda, M., Matsumoto, Y., Ishii, N., Enomoto, S., Yamamoto, H., Tsuchida, N.: The p53 tumor-suppressor gene and ras oncogene mutations in oral squamous-cell carcinoma. Int. J. Cancer <u>52</u>, 867–872 (1992).

Sakai, E., Tsuchida, N.: Most human squamous cell carcinomas in the oral cavity contain mutated p53 tumor-suppressor genes. Oncogene <u>7</u>, 927– 933 (1992).

Sakai, T., Othani, N., McGee, T.L., Robbins, P.D., Dryja, T.P.: Oncogenic germ-line mutations in Sp1 and ATF sites in the human retinoblastoma gene. Nature <u>353</u>, 83–86 (1991).

Salem, G.: Oral lichen planus among 4277 patients from Gizan, Saudi Arabia. Community Dent. Oral Epidemiol. <u>17</u>, 322–324 (1989).

Samman, P.D.: Lichen planus: An analysis of 200 cases. Trans. St. Johns Hosp. Derm. Soc. <u>46</u>, 36–38 (1961).

Sammons, D.W., Adams, L.D., Nishizawa, E.E.: Ultrasensitive silver-based color staining of polypeptides in polyacrylamide gels. Electrophoresis <u>2</u>, 135–141 (1981).

Saranath, D., Bhoite, L.T., Deo, M.G., Koch, W.M., Boyle, J.O., Mao, L., Hakim, J., Hruban, R.H., Sidransky, D.: p53 gene mutations as markers of tumor spread in synchronous oral cancers. Arch. Otolaryngol. Head Neck Surg. <u>120</u>, 943–947 (1994).

Saranath, D., Bhoite, L.T., Deo, M.G.: Molecular lesions in human oral cancer: The indian scene. Eur. J. Cancer Oral Oncol. <u>29B</u>, 107–112 (1993).

Sarnow, P., Ho, Y.S., Williams, J., Levine, A.J.: Adenovirus E1b-58kd tumor antigen and SV40 large tumor antigen are physically associated with the same 54 kd cellular protein in transformed cells. Cell <u>28</u>, 387–394 (1982).

Sasaki, K., Ogino, T., Takahashi, M.: Immunological determination of labeling index on human tumor tissue sections using monclonal anti-BrdUrd antibody. Stain Technol. <u>61</u>, 155–161 (1986).

Schauer, I.E., Siriwardana, S., Langan, T.A., Sclafani, R.A.: Cyclin D1 overexpression vs. retinoblastoma inactivation: Implications for growth control evasion in non-small cell and small cell lung cancer. Proc. Natl. Acad. Sci. USA <u>91</u>, 7827–7831 (1994).

Schell, H., Schönberger, A.: Zur Lokalisationshäufigkeit von benignen und präkanzerösen Leukoplakien und von Karzinomen in der Mundhöhle. Z. Hautkr. <u>62</u>, 798–804 (1987).

Schell, H., Würth, G.: Vergleichende histoautoradiographische und histologische Untersuchungen an benignen und präkanzerösen Leukoplakien der menschlichen Wangenmukosa. Dtsch. Z. Mund KieferGesichtsChir. 12, 212–215 (1988).

Schipper, J.H., Frixen, U.H., Behrens, J., Unger, A., Jahnke, K., Birchmeier, W.: E-Cadherin expression in squamous cell carcinoma of head and neck: Inverse correlation with tumor dedifferentiation and lymph node metastasis. Cancer Res. 51, 6328–6337 (1991).

Schipper, J.H., Kelker, W.: Die Expression der Tumorsuppressorgene p53 und Rb bei Patienten mit Plattenepithelkarzinomen im Kopf- / Halsbereich. HNO 42, 270–274 (1994).

Schlichtholz, B., Legros, Y., Gillet, D., Gaillard, C., Marty, M., Lane, D., Calvo, F., Soussi, T.: The immune response to p53 in breast cancer patients is directed against immunodominant epitopes unrelated to the mutational hot spot . Cancer Res. 52, 6380–6384 (1992).

Schliephake, H., Eckardt, A., Gaida-Martin, S., Pytlik, C.: PCNA / Cyclin-Antikörper als Proliferationsmarker bei Mundschleimhauterkrankungen. Dtsch. Zahnärztl. Z. 47, 845–848 (1992). (english abstract)

Schmidt, H.: Frequency, duration, and localization of lichen planus: A study based on 181 patients. Acta Derm. Venereol. 41, 164–167 (1961).

Schottenfeld, D., Bergad, B.M.: Epidemiology of cancers of the oral cavity, pharynx, and larynx. In: Wittes, R.E. (ed.): Head and Neck Cancer. John Wiley & Sons London 1985, pp 3–12.

Schottenfeld, D.: Alcohol as a co-factor in the etiology of cancer. Cancer 43, 1962–1966 (1979).

Schreiber, E., Matthias, P., Müller, M.M., Schaffner, W.: Rapid detection of octamer binding proteins with 'mini-extracts', prepared from a small number of cells. Nucleic Acids Res. 17, 6419 (1989).

Schriber, E., Matthias, P., Müller, M.M., Schaffer, W.: Rapid detection of octamer binding proteins with 'mini-extracts', prepared from a small number of cells. Nucl. Acids Res. 17, 6419 (1989).

Schroeder, H.E.: Differentiation of human oral stratified epithelia. Karger Basel / München / Paris / London / New York / Sydney 1981.

Schuermann, H.: Zur Karzinomentstehung auf Lichen ruber. Dermatol. Wochenschr. 108, 230 (1939).

Schuuring, E., Verhoeven, E., Mooi, W.J., Michalides, R.J.: Identification and cloning of two overexpressed genes, U21B31 / Prad1 and EMS1, within the amplified chromosome 11q13 region in human carcinomas. Oncogene 7, 355–361 (1992).

Schwartz, L.H., Ozsahin, M., Zhang, G.N., Touboul, E., De Vataire, F., Andolenko, P., Lacau-Saint-Guily, J., Laugier, A., Schlienger, M.: Synchronous and metachronous head and neck carcinomas. Cancer 74, 1933–1938 (1994).

Scott, R., Wilke, M.S., Wille, J.J., Pittelkow, M.R., Hsu, B.M., Kasperbauer, J.L.: Human squamous carcinoma cells express complex defects in the control of cell proliferation and differentiation. Am. J. Pathol. 133, 374–380 (1988).

Scott, R.J., Hall, P.A., Haldane, J.S., van Noorden, S., Price, Y., Lane, D.P., Wright, N.A.: A comparison of immunohistochemical markers of cell proliferation with experimentally determined growth fraction. J. Path. 165, 173–178 (1991).

Scully, C., El-Kom, M.: Lichen planus: Review and update on pathogenesis. J. Oral Pathol. 14, 431– 458 (1985).

Scully, C.: Oncogenes, onco-suppressors, carcinogenesis and oral cancer. Br. Dent. J. 173, 53– 59 (1992).

Scully, C.: Oncogenes, tumor suppressors and viruses in oral squamous carcinoma. J. Oral Pathol. Med. 22, 337–347 (1993).

Scully, C.: Review of the Literature. In: Millard, H.D., Mason, D.K. (eds.): World Workshop on Oral Medicine. Year Book Medical Publisher Chicago 1989, pp 135–184.

Scully, C.: Viruses and oral squamous cell carcinoma. Eur. J. Cancer Oral Oncol. 28B, 57–59 (1992).

Seitz, H.K., Czygan, P., Waldherr, R., Veith, S., Raedsch, R., Kassmodel, H., Kommerell, B.: Enhancement of 1,2-dimethylhydrazine-induced rectal carcinogenesis following chronic ethanol consumption in the rat. Gastroenterology 86, 886–891 (1984).

Seitz, H.K., Simanowsky, U.A.: Alcohol and carcinogenesis. Ann. Rev. Nutr. 8, 99–119 (1988).

Selby, C.P., Sancar, A.: Molecular mechanism of transcription-repair coupling Science 260, 53–58 (1993).

Sellars, S.L.: Epidemiology of oral cancer. Otolaryng. Clin. North Am. 12, 45–55 (1979).

Sen, P.: Chromosome 9 anomalies as the primary clonal alteration in a case of squamous cell carcinoma of the epiglottis. Cancer Genet. Cytogenet. 66, 23–27 (1993).

Sen, S., d'Incalci, M.: Apoptosis. Biochemical events and relevance to cancer chemotherapy. FEBS Lett. 307, 122–127 (1992).

Serra, A., Gaidano, G.L., Revello, D., Guerrasio, A., Ballerini, P., Dalla Favera, R., Saglio, G.: A new TaqI polymorphism in the p53 gene. Nucleic Acids Res. 20, 928 (1992).

Serrano, M., Hannon, G.J., Beach, D.: A new regulatory motif in cell-cycle control causing specific inhibition of cyclin D / CDK4. Nature 366, 704–707 (1993).

Seto, E., Usheva, A., Zambetti, G.P., Momand, J., Horikoshi, N., Weinmann, R., Levine, A.J., Shenk, T.: Wild-type p53 binds to the TATA-binding protein and represses transcription. Proc. Natl. Acad. Sci. USA 89, 12028–12032 (1992).

Sewing, A., Rönicke, V., Bürger, C., Funk, M., Müller, R.: Alternative splicing of human cyclin E. J. Cell Sci. 107, 581–588 (1994).

Shaulsky, G., Goldfinger, N., Tosky, M.S., Leviend A.J., Rotter, V.: Nuclear localization is essential for the activity of p53 protein. Oncogene 6, 2055– 2065 (1991).

Shen, D.-W., Real, F.X., DeLeo A.B., Old, L.J., Marks, P.A., Rifkind, R.A.: Protein p53 and inducer-mediated erythroleukemia cell commitment to terminal cell division. Proc. Natl. Acad. Sci. USA 80, 5919–5922 (1983).

Sherr, C.J.: G1 Phase progression: Cycling on cue. Cell 79, 551–555 (1994).

Sherr, C.J.: Mammalian G1 cyclins. Cell 73, 1059–1065 (1993).

Shew, J.-Y., Ling, N., Yang, X., Fodstad, O., Lee, W.-H.: Antibodies detecting abnormalities of the retinoblastoma susceptibility gene product (pp110^{RB}) in osteosarcomas and synovial sarcomas. Oncogene Res. 1, 205–214 (1989).

Shin, D.M., Kim, J., Ro, J.Y., Hittelman, J., Roth, J.A., Hong, W.K., Hittelman, W.N.: Activation of p53 gene expression in premalignant lesions during head and neck tumorigenesis. Cancer Res. 54, 321–326 (1994).

Shin, D.M., Voravud, N., Ro, J.Y., Lee, J.S., Hong W.K., Hittelman, W.N.: Sequential increases in proliferating cell nuclear antigen expression in head and neck tumorigenesis: A potential biomarker. J. Natl. Cancer Inst. 85, 971–978 (1993).

Shingaki, S., Suzuki, I., Nakajima, T., Kawasaki, T.: Evaluation of histopathologic parameters in predicting cervical lymph node metastasis of oral and oropharyngeal carcinomas. Oral Surg. Oral Med. Oral Pathol. 66, 683–688 (1988).

Shivji, M.K., Kenny, M.K., Wood, R.D.: Proliferating cell nuclear antigen is required for DNA excision repair. Cell 69, 367–374 (1992).

Shklar, G.: Lichen planus as an oral ulcerative disease. Oral Surg. Oral Med. Oral Pathol. 33, 376–388 (1972).

Shklar, G.: Oral leukoplakia. New Engl. J. Med. 315, 1544–1546 (1986).

Sidransky, D., Boyle, J., Koch, W.: Molecular screening. Prospects for a new approach. Arch. Otolaryng. Head Neck Surg. 119, 1187–1190 (1993).

Sigurgeirsson, B.: Skin disease and malignancy. An epidemiological study. Karolinska Insitute Stockholm 1992.

Silverman, S. Jr., Barghava, K., Mani, N.J., Smith, L.W., Malaowalla, A.M.: Malignant transformation and natural history of oral leukoplakia in 57,518 industrial workers of Gujarat, India. Cancer 38, 1790–1795 (1976).

Silverman, S. Jr., Gorsky, M., Lozada-Nur, F., Giannotti, K.: A prospective study of findings and management in 214 patients with oral lichen planus. Oral Surg. 72, 665–670 (1991).

Silverman, S. Jr., Gorsky, M., Lozada-Nur, F.: A prospective follow-up of 570 patients with oral lichen planus: Persistence, remission, and malignant association. Oral Surg. Oral Med. Oral Pathol. 60, 30–34 (1985).

Silverman, S. Jr., Griffith, M.: Studies on oral lichen planus II. Follow-up on 200 patients, clinical characteristics and associated malignancy. Oral Surg. Oral Med. Oral Pathol. 37, 705–710 (1974).

Singh, P., Wong, S.H., Hong, W.: Overexpression of E2F-1 in rat embryo fibroblasts leads to neoplastic transformation. EMBO J. 13, 3329–3338 (1994).

Slaughter, D.P., Southwick, H.W., Smejkal, W.: "Field cancerization" in oral stratified squamous epithelium: Clinical implications of multicentric origin. Cancer 6, 963–968 (1953).

Slebos, R.J., Lee, M.H., Plunkett, B.S., Kessis, T.D., Williams, B.O., Jacks, T., Hedrick, L., Kastan, M.B., Cho, K.R.: p53-dependent G1 arrest involves pRB-related proteins and is disrupted by the human papillomavirus 16 E7 oncoprotein. Proc. Natl. Acad. Sci. USA 91, 5320–5324 (1994).

Slingerland, J.M., Hengst, L., Pan, C.H., Alexander, D., Stampfer, M.R., Reed, S.I.: A novel inhibitor of cyclin-Cdk activity detected in transforming growth factor beta-arrested epithelial cells. Mol. Cell Biol. 14, 3683–3694 (1994).

Slootweg, P.J., Koole, R., Hordijk, G.J.: The presence of p53 protein in relation to Ki-67 as cellular proliferation marker in head and neck squamous cell carcinoma and adjacent dysplastic mucosa. Eur. J. Cancer Oral Onc. 30B, 138–141 (1994).

Smets, L.A.: Programmed cell death (apoptosis) and response to anti-cancer drugs. Anti-Cancer Drugs 5, 3–9 (1994).

Smith, C., Pindborg, J.J., Binnie, W.H. (eds.): Oral cancer—epidemiology, etiology, and pathology. Hemisphere Publishing Corporation New York / Washington / Philadelphia / London 1990.

Smith, M.L., Chen, I.-T., Zhan, Q., Bae, I., Cehen, S.-Y., Gilmer, T.M., Kastan, M.B., O'Conor, P.M., Fornace, A.J.: Interaction of the p53-regulated protein Gadd45 with proliferating cell nuclear antigen. Science 266, 1377–1380 (1994).

Somers, K.D., Merrick, M.A., Lopez, M.E., Incognito, L.S., Schlechter, G.L., Casey, G.: Frequent p53 mutations in head and neck cancer. Cancer Res 52, 5997–6000 (1992).

Spiro, R.H., Huvos, A.G., Wong, G.Y., Spiro, J.D., Gnecco, C.A.,Strong, E.W.: Predictive value of tumor thickness in squamous carcinoma confined to the tongue and floor of the mouth. Am. J. Surg. 152, 345–350 (1986).

Sporn, M.B., Dunlop, N.M., Newton, D.L., Smith, J.M.: Prevention of chemical carcinogenesis by vitamin A and its synthetic analogs (retinoids). Fed. Proc. 35, 1332–1338 (1976).

Steinbeck, R.G., Moege, J., Heselmeyer, K.M., Klebe, W., Neugebauer, W., Borg, B., Auer, G.U.: DNA content and PCNA immunoreactivity in oral precancerous and cancerous lesions. Eur. J. Cancer Oral Oncol. 29B, 279–284 (1993).

Steinberg, B.M., Auborn, K.J.: Papillomaviruses in head and neck disease: Pathophysiology and possible regulation. J. Cell. Biochem. Suppl 17F, 155–164 (1993).

Stich, H.F., Hornby, A.P., Dunn, B.P.: A pilot beta-carotene intervention trial with inuits using smokeless tobacco. Int. J. Cancer 36, 321–327 (1985).

Stich, H.F., Ronsin, M.P., Hornby, A.P., Mathew, B., Sankaranarayanan, R., Nair, M.K.: Remission of oral leukoplakias and micronuclei in tobacco / betel quid chewers treated with beta-carotene plus vitamin A. Int. J. Cancer 42, 195–199 (1988).

Störkel, S., Reichert, T., Reiffen, K.A., Wagner, W.: EGFR and PCNA expression in oral squamous cell carcinomas—a valuable tool in estimating the patient's prognosis. Eur. J. Cancer Oral Onc. 29B, 273–277 (1993).

Sugár, L., Bánóczy, J.: Untersuchungen bei Präkanzerose der Mundschleimhaut. Dtsch. Zahn Mund Kieferheilkd. 30, 132–140 (1959).

Sugerman, P.B., Rollason, P.A., Savage, N.W., Seymour, G.J.: Suppressor cell function in oral lichen planus. J. Dent. Res. 71, 1916–1919 (1992).

Sugerman, P.B., Savage, N.W., Walsh, L.J., Seymour, G.J.: Disease mechanisms in oral lichen planus. A possible role for autoimmunity. Aust. J. Dermtol. 34, 63–69 (1993).

Suzuki, K., Chen, R.-B., Nomura, T., Nakajima, T.: Flow cytometric analysis of primary and metastatic squamous cell carcinomas of the oral and maxillofacial region. J. Oral Maxillofac. Surg. 52, 855–861 (1994).

Szekely, L., Jian, W.-Q., Bulic-Jakus, F., Rosen, A., Ringertz, N., Klein, G., Wiman, K.G.: Cell type and differentiation dependent heterogenity in retinoblastoma protein expression in SCID mouse fetuses. Cell Growth Differ. 1, 17–25 (1992).

T'Ang, A., Varley, J.M., Chakraborty, S., Murphree, A.L., Fung, Y.-K.: Structural rearrangement of the retinoblastoma gene in human breast carcinoma. Science 242, 263–266 (1988).

Thomas, S., Brennan, J., Martel, G., Frazer, I., Montesano, R., Sidransky, D., Hollstein, M.: Mutations in the conserved regions of p53 are infrequent in betel-associated oral cancers from Papua New Guinea. Cancer Res. 54, 3588–3593 (1994).

Thompson, A.M., Anderson, T.J., Condie, A., Prosser, J., Chetty, U., Carter, D.C., Evans, H.J., Steel, C.M.: p53 allele losses, mutations and expression in breast cancer and their relationship to clinico-pathological parameters. Int. J. Cancer 50, 528–532 (1992).

Thorn, J.J., Holmstrup, P., Rindum, J., Pindborg, J.J.: Course of various clinical forms of oral lichen planus. A prospective follow-up study of 611 patients. J. Oral Pathol. 17, 213–218 (1988).

Tischendorf, L., Giehler, U.: Studien zur Dignität der Leukoplakien von Mundschleimhaut und Lippen. Dtsch. Z. Mund Kiefer GesichtsChir. 14, 301–305 (1990).

Tompkins, J.K.: Lichen planus: A statistical study of forty-one cases. Arch. Derm. 71, 515–519 (1955).

Toyoshima, H., Hunter, T.: p27, a novel inhibitor of G1 cyclin-Cdk protein kinase activity, is related to p21. Cell 78, 67–74 (1994).

Tsuji, T., Sasaki, K., Kimura, Y., Yamada, K., Mori, M., Shinozaki, F.: Measurement of proliferating cell nuclear antigen (PCNA) and its clinical application in oral cancers. Int. J. Oral Maxillofac. Surg. 21, 369–372 (1992a).

Tsuji, T., Shrestha, P., Yamada, K., Takagi, H., Shinozaki, F., Sasaki, K., Maeda, K., Mori, M.: Proliferating cell nuclear antigen in malignant and pre-malignant lesions of epithelial origin in the oral cavity and the skin: An immunohistochemical study. Virchows Archiv A. Pathol. Anat. 420, 377–383 (1992b).

Tsuruta, H., Sakamoto, H., Onda, M., Terada, M.: Amplification and overexpression of EXP1 and EXP2 / cyclin D1 genes in human esophageal carcinomas. Biochem. Biophys. Res. Comm. 196, 1529–1536 (1993).

Tuyns, A.J., Péquignot, G., Jensen, O.M.: Le cancer de l`oesophage en Ille-et-Vilaine en fonction des niveaux de consommation d`alcool et de tabac: Des risques qui se multiplient. Bull. Cancer 64, 45–60 (1977).

Tyldesley, W.R.: Oral lichen planus. Br. J. Oral Surg. 11, 187–206 (1974).

Tytor, M., Olofsson, J., Ledin, T., Brunk, U., Klintenberg, C.: Squamous cell carcinoma of the oral cavity. A review of 176 cases with application of malignancy grading and DNA measurements. Clin. Otolaryngol. 15, 235–251 (1990).

Ullrich, S.J., Mercer, W.E., Apella, E.: Human wild-type p53 adopts a unique conformational and phosphorylation state in vivo during growth arrest of glioblastoma cells. Oncogene 7, 1635–1643 (1992).

Urist, M.M., O'Brien, C.J., Soong, S.-J., Visscher, D.W., Maddox, W.A.: Squamous cell carcinoma of the buccal mucosa: Analysis of prognostic factors. Am. J. Surg. 154, 411–414 (1987).

van der Riet, P., Nawroz, H., Hruban, R.H., Corio, R., Tokino, K., Koch, W., Sidransky, D.: Frequent loss of chromosome 9p21-22 early in head and neck cancer progression. Cancer Res. 54, 1156–1158 (1994).

van der Waal, I.: Oral precancerous lesions—present knowledge. Dtsch. Zahnärztl. Z. 47, 860–864 (1992).

van Dyke, D.L., Worsham, M.J., Benninger, M.S., Krause, C.J., Baker, S.R., Wolf, G.T., Drumheller, T., Tilley, B.C., Carey, T.E.: Recurrent cytogenetic abnormalities in squamous cell carcinomas of the head and neck region. Genes Chrom. Cancer. 9, 192–206 (1994).

van Vuuren, A.J., Appeldoorn, E., Odijk, H., Yasui, A., Jaspers, N.G., Bootsma, D., Hoeijmakers, J.H.: Evidence for a repair enzyme complex involving ERCC1 and complementing activities of ERCC4, ERCC11 and xeroderma pigmentosum group F. EMBO J. 12, 3693–3701 (1993).

Varley, J.M., Armour, J., Swallow, J.E., Jeffreys, A.J., Ponder, B.A., T'Ang, A., Fung, Y.-K., Brammar, W.J., Walker, R.A.: The retinoblastoma gene is frequently altered leading to loss of expression in primary breast tumors. Oncogene 4, 725–729 (1989).

Vesper, M., Schmelzle, R., Ritter-Kröhn, R., Günzl, H.-J.: Vergleichende Untersuchung histologisch gesicherter Leukoplakien im Cavum oris. Dtsch. Zahnärztl. Z. 47, 867–869 (1992). (english abstract)

Vincent, R.G., Marchetta, F.: The relationship of the use of tobacco and alcohol to cancer of the oral cavity, pharynx or larnyx. Am. J. Surg. 106, 501–505 (1963).

Vincent, S.D., Fotos, P.G., Baker, K.A., Williams, T.P.: Oral lichen planus: The clinical, historical and therapeutic features of 100 cases. Oral Surg. Oral Med. Oral Pathol. 70, 165–171 (1990).

Vogelstein, B., Kinzler, K.W.: p53 function and dysfunction. Cell 70, 523–526 (1992).

Vojtesek, B., Lane, D.P.: Regulation of p53 protein expression in human breast cancer cell lines. J. Cell Sci. 105, 607–612 (1993).

Vokes, E.E., Weichselbaum, R.R., Lippman, S.M., Hong, W.K.: Head and Neck Cancer. New Engl. J. Med. 328, 184–194 (1993).

von Jänner, M., Muissus, E., Rohde, B.: Lichen planus als fakultative Präkanzerose. Dermatol. Wschr. 153, 513–518 (1967).

Voravud, N., Shin, D.M., Ro, J.Y., Lee, J.S., Hong, W.K., Hittelman, W.N.: Increased polysomies of chromosomes 7 and 17 during head and neck multistage tumorigenesis. Cancer Res. 53, 2874–2883 (1993).

Voute, A.B., de Jong, W.F., Schulten E.A., Snow, G.B., van der Waal, I.: Possible premalignant character of oral lichen planus: The Amsterdam experience. J. Oral Pathol. Med. 21, 326–329 (1992).

Vrabec, D.P.: Multiple primary malignancies of the upper aerodigestive system. Ann. Otol. Rhinol. Laryng. 88, 846–854 (1979).

Waber, P.G., Chen, J., Nisen, P.D.: Infrequency of MDM2 gene amplification in pediatric solid tumors and lack of association with p53 mutations in adult squamous cell carcinomas. Cancer Res. 53, 6028–6030 (1993).

Waga, S., Hannon, G.J., Beach, D., Stillman, B.: The p21 inhibitor of cyclin-dependent kinases controls DNA replication by interaction with PCNA. Nature 369, 574–578 (1994).

Wahi, P.N., Mital, V:P., Lahiri, B., Luthra, U.K., Seth, R.K., Arora, G.D.: Epidemiological study of precancerous lesions of the oral cavity: A preliminary report. Indian J. Med. Res. 58, 1361–1391 (1970).

Waldron, C.A., Shafer, W.G.: Leukoplakia revisited: A clinicopathologic study 3256 oral leukoplakias. Cancer 36, 1386–1392 (1975).

Walsh, L.J., Ishii, T., Savage, N.W., Gemmell, E., Seymour, G.J.: Immunohistologic analysis of epithelial cell populations in oral lichen planus. J. Oral Pathol. Med. 19, 177–181 (1990).

Wang, T.C., Cardiff, R.D., Zukerberg, L., Lees, E., Arnold, A., Schmidt, E.V.: Mammary hyperplasia and carcinoma in MMTV-cyclin D1 transgenic mice. Nature 369, 669–671 (1994a).

Wang, X.W., Forrester, K., Yeh, H., Feitelson, M.A., Gu, J.-R., Harris, C.C.: Hepatitis B virus X protein inhibits p53 sequence-specific DNA binding, transcriptional activity, and association with transcription factor ERCC3. Proc. Natl. Acad. Sci. USA 91, 2230–2234 (1994b).

Warin, R.P.: Epithelioma following lichen planus of the mouth. Br.J. Dermatol. 72, 288–291 (1960).

Warnakulasuriya, K.A., Johnson, N.W.: Expression of p53 mutant nuclear phosphoprotein in oral carcinoma and potentially malignant oral lesions. J. Oral Pathol. Med. 21, 404–408 (1992).

Waseem, N.H., Lane, D.P.: Monoclonal antibody analysis of the proliferating cell nuclear antigen (PCNA). J. Cell Sci. 96, 121–129 (1990).

Watling, D.L., Gown, A.M., Coltrera, M.D.: Overexpression of p53 in head and neck cancer. Head Neck 14, 437–444 (1992).

Weinberg, R.A.: The retinoblastoma gene and gene product. In: Franks, L.M.: Cancer Surveys, Vol. 12: Levine, A.J., (ed.): Tumor suppressor genes, the cell cycle and cancer. Cold Spring Harbor Laboratory Press, Cold Spring Harbor 1992, pp 43–58.

White, E.: p53, guardian of Rb. Nature 371, 21–22 (1994).

Whyte, P., Buchkovich, K.J., Horowitz, J.M., Friend, S.H., Raybuck, M., Weinberg, R.A., Harlow, E.: Association between an oncogene and an anti-oncogene: The adenovirus E1A proteins bind to the retinoblastoma gene product. Nature 334, 124– 129 (1988).

Wickham, L.F.: Un signe pathognomique du Lichen de Wilson (lichen plan). Ann. Dermatol. Syph. 6, 517–520 (1895).

Wiethege, T., Voss, B., Müller, K.-M.: Detection of MDM2-proto-oncogene in paraffin embedded human bronchial epithelium. J. Cancer Res. Clin. Oncol. 120, 222–225 (1994).

Williams, M.E., Gaffey, M.J., Weiss, L.M., Wilczynski, S.P., Schuuring, E., Levine, P.A.: Chromosome 11Q13 amplification in head and neck squamous cell carcinoma. Arch. Otolaryngol. Head Neck Surg. 119, 1238–1243 (1993).

Williger, F.: Lichen ruber planus und Karzinom. Vjschr. Zahnh. 1, 58–61 (1924).

Wilsch, L., Hornstein, O.P., Brüning, H., Schwipper, V., Lösel, F., Schönberger, A., Gunselmann, W., Prestele, H.: Orale Leukoplakien II. Ergebnisse einer 1jährigen poliklinischen Pilotstudie. Dtsch. Zahnärztl. Z. 33, 132–142 (1978).

Wilson, E.: On leichen planus. J. Cutan. Med. Dis. Skin 3, 117–132 (1869).

Winston, J.T., Pledger, W.J.: Growth factor regulation of cyclin D1 mRNA expression through protein synthesis-dependent and -independent mechanisms. Mol. Biol. Cell 4, 1133–1144 (1993).

Wintzer, H.-O., Zipfel, I., Schulte-Mönting, J., Hellerich, U., von Kleist, S.: Ki-67 immunostaining in human breast tumors and its relationship to prognosis. Cancer 67, 421–429 (1991).

Won, K.-A., Xiong, Y., Beach, D., Gilman, M.Z.: Growth-regulated expression of D-type cyclin genes in human diploid fibroblasts. Proc. Natl. Acad. Sci. USA 89, 9910–9914 (1992).

Wong, R.L., Katz, M.E., Ogata, K., Tan, E.M., Cohen, S.: Inhibition of nuclear DNA synthesis by an autoantibody to proliferating cell nuclear antigen / cyclin. Cell. Immunol. 110, 443-448 (1987).

Woods, K.V., Shillitoe, E.J., Spitz, M.R., Schantz, S.P., Adler-Storthz, K.: Analysis of human papillomavirus DNA in oral squamous cell carcinomas. J. Oral Pathol. Med. 22, 101-108 (1993).

World Health Organization Collaborating Center for Oral Precancerous Lesions.: Definition of leukoplakia and related lesions: An aid to studies in oral precancer. Oral Surg. Oral Med. Oral Pathol. 46, 518–539 (1978).

Worsham, M.J., van Dyke, D.L., Grenman, S.E., Grenman, R., Hopkins, M., Roberts, J.A., Gasser, K.M., Schwartz, D.R., Carey, T.E.: Consistent chromosome abnormality in squamous cell carcinoma of the vulva. Genes Chrom. Cancer 3, 420–432 (1991).

Wu, F., Bui, K.C., Buckley, S., Warburton, D.: Cell cycle-dependent expression of cyclin D1 and a 45 kD protein in human A549 lung carcinoma cells. Am. J. Respir. Cell. Mol. Biol. 10, 437–447 (1994).

Wu, X., Bayle, J.H., Olson, D., Levine, A.J.: The p53-mdm-2 autoregulatory feedback loop. Genes Dev. 7, 1126–1132 (1993).

Wu, X., Levine, A.J.: p53 and E2F-1 cooperate to mediate apoptosis. Proc. Natl. Acad. Sci. USA 91, 3602–3606 (1994).

Wustrow, T.P.U., Issing, W.J.: Immune defects in patients with head and neck cancer. Anticancer Res. 13, 2507–2520 (1993).

Wynder, E.L., Bross, I.J., Feldman, R.M.: A study of the etiological factors in cancer of the mouth. Cancer 10, 1300–1323 (1957).

Wynder, E.L., Bross, I.J.: Aetiological factors in mouth cancer: An approach to its prevention. Br. Med. J. 1137–1143 (1957).

Wynder, E.L., Hoffman, D.: Tobacco and tobacco smoke. Semin. Oncol. 3, 5–15 (1976).

Wynder, E.L., Hoffmann, D.: Experimental tobacco carcinogenesis. Science 162, 862–871 (1968).

Xiong, Y., Zhang, H., Beach, D.: D type cyclins associate with multiple protein kinases and the DNA Replication and Repair Factor PCNA. Cell 71, 505–514 (1992a).

Xiong, Y., Hannon, G.J., Zhang, H., Casso, D., Kobayashi, R., Beach, D.: p21 is a universal inhibitor of cyclin kinases. Nature 366, 701–704 (1993b).

Xiong, Y., Menninger, J., Beach, D., Ward, D.C.: Molecular cloning and chromosomal mapping of CCND Genes encoding human D-type cyclins. Genomics 13, 575–584 (1992b).

Xiong, Y., Zhang, H., Beach, D.: Subunit rearrangement of the cyclin-dependent kinases is associated with cellular transformation. Genes Dev. 7, 1572–1583 (1993a).

Xu, H.-J., Hu, S.-X., Benedict, W.F.: Lack of nuclear RB protein staining in G0 / middle G1 cells: Correlation to changes in total RB protein level. Oncogene 6, 1139–1146 (1991).

Xu, H.-J., Hu, S.-X., Hashimoto, T., Takahashi, R., Benedict, W.F.: The retinoblastoma susceptibility gene product: A characteristic pattern in normal cells and abnormal expression in malignant cells. Oncogene 4, 807–812 (1989).

Yen, A., Varvayanis, S.: Late dephosphorylation of the RB protein in G2 during the process of induced cell differentiation. Exp. Cell Res, 214, 250–257 (1994).

Yeudall, W.A.: Human papillomaviruses and oral neoplasia. Eur. J. Cancer Oral Oncol. 28B, 61–66 (1992).

Yew, P.R., Berk, A.J.: Inhibition of p53 transactivation required for transformation by the adenovirus early 1B protein. Nature 357, 82–85 (1992).

Yin, X.-Y., Smith, M.L., Whiteside, T.L., Johnson, J.T., Herberman, R.B., Locker, J.: Abnormalities in the p53 gene in tumors and cell lines of human squamous-cell carcinomas of the head and neck. Int. J. Cancer 54, 322–327 (1993).

Yokota, J., Wada, M., Shimosato, Y., Terada, M., Sugimura, T.: Loss of heterozygosity on chromosomes 3, 13, and 17 in small-cell carcinoma and on chromosome 3 in adenocarcinoma of the lung. Proc. Natl. Acad. Sci. USA 84, 9252–9256 (1987).

Yonish-Rouach, E., Grunwald, D., Wilder, S., Kimichi, A., May, E., Lawrence, J.-J., May, P., Oren, M.: p53-mediated cell death: Relationship to cell cycle control. Mol. Cell. Biol. 13, 1415–1423 (1993).

Yoo, G.H., Xu, H.J., Brennan, J.A., Westra, W., Hruban, R.H., Koch, W., Benedict, W.F., Sidransky, D.: Infrequent inactivation of the retinoblastoma gene despite frequent loss of chromosome 13q in head and neck squamous cell carcinoma. Cancer Res. 54, 4603–4606 (1994).

Yunis, J.J., Ramsey, N.: Retinoblastoma and subband deletion of chromosome 13. Am. J. Dis. Child. 132, 161–163 (1978).

Zachariah, J., Matthew, B., Varma, N.A., Iqbal, A.M., Pindborg, J.J.: Frequency of oral lesions among 5,000 individuals in Trivandrum, South India. J. All. India Dent. Assoc. 38, 290–294 (1966).

Zambetti, G.P., Bargonetti, J., Walker, K., Prives, C., Levine, A.J.: Wild-type p53 mediates positive regulation of gene expression through a specific DNA sequence element. Genes Dev. 6, 1142– 1152 (1992).

Zhang, H., Xiong, Y., Beach, D.: Proliferating cell nuclear antigen and p21 are components of multiple cell cycle kinase complexes. Mol. Biol. Cell 4, 897–906 (1993).

Zöller, J., Flentje, M., Sinn, P., Born, I.A.: "Nukelolar Organizer Region" and "Ki-67" als zellkinetische Parameter für orale Dysplasien und Plattenepithelkarzinome. Dtsch. Z. Mund Kiefer GesichtsChir. 17, 185–190 (1993).

Zöller, J., Maier, H., Hofele, Ch., Massa, J., Born, I.A.: Zum Stellenwert von Alkohol, Tabak und Speichelsekretion in der Ätiologie von oralen Dysplasien. Dtsch. Zahnärztl. Z. 47, 848–851 (1992). (english abstract)

Zöller, J.: Zur malignen Transformation des Epithels der Mundschleimhaut unter Chemotherapie und Chemoprevention. Med. Habil. Heidelberg 1991.